# CGP

# Key Stage Three
# Biology, Physics & Chemistry

# CGP

## Answer Book

### For the **Higher Level** Workbooks

# Contents

## Biology

## Chemistry

## Physics

Published by CGP

ISBN: 978 1 84146 507 4

www.cgpbooks.co.uk

Printed by Elanders Ltd, Newcastle upon Tyne.
Clipart from Corel®

# Answers

## Biology
### Section 1 — Cells and Respiration
#### Pages 1-2 — The Microscope
**Q1**
    A — Eyepiece lens
    B — Body tube
    C — Rough focusing knob
    D — Fine focusing knob
    E — High and low power objective lenses
    F — Stage

**Q2** a) The rough focusing knob and the fine focusing knob.
    b) i) The stage.
       ii) The slide is clipped to the stage / held in place by clips.
    c) To magnify the object.

**Q3** a) The mirror.
    b) The lowest powered objective lens.
    c) i) The rough focusing knob.
       ii) She should move it down to just above the slide.
    d) i) The fine focusing knob.
       ii) Away from the slide.
       iii) To make sure the lens and slide don't crash together.
    e) She could switch to using a higher powered objective lens.

#### Pages 3-5 — Cells
**Q1** a) nucleus
    b) cell membrane
    c) cell wall
    d) mitochondria
    e) vacuole
    f) cytoplasm
    g) chloroplast

| Both cells have | Only plant cells have |
|---|---|
| 1) cell membrane | 1) cell wall |
| 2) nucleus | 2) chloroplasts |
| 3) cytoplasm | 3) vacuole |
| 4) mitochondria | |

**Q2** The nucleus.
**Q3** The mitochondria.
**Q4** Chloroplast — contains chlorophyll for photosynthesis.
Vacuole — large space filled with sap.
Mitochondria — where most of the reactions for aerobic respiration take place.
Cytoplasm — jelly-like stuff where most of the reactions happen.
Nucleus — controls what the cell does.
Cell membrane — thin skin around the cell.
Cell wall — outer coating which gives support to the cell.

**Q5** a) Because they are too small to see with just your eyes.
    b) To make the parts of the cells easier to see.
    c)

| | Cytoplasm | Nucleus | Cell wall | Vacuole |
|---|---|---|---|---|
| Cheek cell | ✓ | ✓ | | |
| Leaf mesophyll cell | ✓ | ✓ | ✓ | ✓ |

**Q6** a) It holds the cell together and controls what goes in and out of the cell.
    b) i) E.g. a cell wall is a rigid outer coating but a cell membrane is just a thin skin. / The cell wall only provides support for the cell but the cell membrane also controls what goes in and out of the cell.
       ii) cellulose

**Q7** a) Having only one cell.
    b) i) E.g. has a flagellum / contains chloroplasts
       ii) E.g. *Euglena* live in water, so having a tail-like structure helps them to swim. / Having chloroplasts means that *Euglena* can make their own food.

#### Page 6 — Cell Organisation
**Q1** a) cell, tissue, organ, organism
    b) yes
**Q2** a) Because there is a lot of carbon dioxide inside the cell but not much outside the cell.
    b) The cell membrane.
    c) The oxygen molecules will move into the cell because there is lots of oxygen outside the cell but not much inside the cell.

#### Pages 7-11 — Respiration
**Q1** Inside the cells in your body **glucose** is used to produce **energy**. This process is called **respiration**. All living things need energy for processes such as **movement**, **growth** and **reproduction**.

**Q2** a) The process of releasing energy from glucose.
    b) Respiration takes place in all types of living organism.
    c) Aerobic and anaerobic.

**Q3** a) Aerobic and anaerobic should both be ticked.
    b) Aerobic should be ticked.
    c) Aerobic and anaerobic should both be ticked.
    d) Aerobic should be ticked.

**Q4** a) Glucose and oxygen.
    b) Carbon dioxide and water.
    c) Energy is released, which is used for e.g. building proteins, muscle contraction and keeping warm.
    d) $B + C \rightarrow A + D + E$
    e) In the mitochondria.

**Q5** glucose → lactic acid + energy
glucose → carbon dioxide + ethanol + energy

**Q6** a) He can use the sugar to produce more energy through respiration.
    b) Anaerobic respiration is respiration without oxygen.
    c) He is starting to respire anaerobically because he can't get enough oxygen to his muscle cells.
    d) Anaerobic respiration produces lactic acid which is starting to build up in Tim's muscles.

**Q7** a) The yeast need sugar to respire.
    b) The yeast must respire anaerobically to make ethanol, so they must be kept away from the oxygen in the air.
    c) fermentation

2

# Answers

**Q8 a)** The soda lime is used to absorb any carbon dioxide that is already in the air. This means that any carbon dioxide in tube B must have been produced by the cricket respiring.

**b) i)** The limewater in tube A will stay colourless.

**ii)** The limewater in tube B will turn cloudy.

**c)** There will be less oxygen present in tube B than in tube A.

**d)** They could set up a second set of apparatus and leave it for the same amount of time, but not put a cricket in the jar.

**Q9 a)** E.g. only aerobic respiration requires oxygen to react with the glucose. Aerobic respiration produces carbon dioxide and water, where as anaerobic respiration produces lactic acid. They release different amounts of energy.

**b) i)** Aerobic respiration.

**ii)** Because it is more efficient.

**Q10 a)** aerobic respiration

**b)** ethanol

**c)** energy

**d)** carbon dioxide

**e)** water

**f)** oxygen

**g)** glucose

**h)** anaerobic respiration

**i)** lactic acid

**j)** fermentation

## Section 2 — Humans as Organisms
### Pages 12-15 — Nutrition

**Q1** What we eat — intake of nourishing substances.

**Q2 a) i)** Used as fuel for the body.

**ii)** Used as a store of energy (which you use if your body runs out of carbohydrates).

**iii)** Needed for growth and to repair damaged areas.

**iv)** Needed (in small amounts) to keep many vital processes happening in the body.

**b)** minerals

**c)** All chemical reactions in the body take place in water (and 75% of the body is made up of water).

**d)** A disease directly resulting from a lack of essential nutrients.

**e)** If you don't eat enough fruit and vegetables you may not get enough vitamins (e.g. vitamin C) in your diet and may show signs of vitamin deficiencies (e.g. scurvy). Also, you may not get enough fibre in your diet. You need fibre to help food move through your digestive system.

**Q3 a)** E.g. he needs to take food that is high in carbohydrates, which sausages are not.

**b)** cereal bars

**Q4 a)** carbohydrates

**b)** Hibran flakes

**c)** Fibre helps food move through your digestive system.

**d)** No. Different types of nutrients are needed in different amounts.

**Q5 a) i)** If you take in more energy from your diet than you use up, your body stores the extra energy as fat. So you put on weight.

**ii)** E.g. high blood pressure / heart disease.

**b)** E.g. starvation can cause children to grow more slowly than they should / can make you more likely to get infections and diseases / can lead to irregular periods in women.

**Q6 a)** Carbohydrates and lipids/fats.

**b) i)** E.g. every cell needs energy. The bigger you are, the more cells you have, and so the more energy you need. / You need energy to move, and it takes more energy to move a bigger mass.

**ii)** How active you are.

**c)** A professional athlete, because he/she is likely to be more active and so have the largest energy demands.

**Q7** Daily BER (kJ/day) = 5.4 × 24 × body mass (kg)
Mihir's BER = 5.4 × 24 × 65
**= 8424 kJ/day**

**Q8 a)** Daily BER (kJ/day) = 5.4 × 24 × body mass (kg)
Sheena's BER = 5.4 × 24 × 60
**= 7776 kJ/day**

**b)** Sheena's BER is 7776 kJ/day
For her 1 hour run she needs 3000 kJ.
For her swim she needs 0.5 × 1500 = 750 kJ
So in total on Thursday she needs:
7776 + 3000 + 750 = **11526 kJ**

### Pages 16-20 — Digestion

**Q1** The process of **digestion** is the breakdown of **food** into soluble substances, and the passage of these substances into the **blood**. The food molecules are too **large** to pass through the gut wall, so they are broken down first by special chemicals called **enzymes**.

**Q2 a) i)** Chewing/churning the food to break it into small pieces.

**ii)** Using enzymes to break up big food molecules into smaller ones.

**b)** The teeth chew up the food and mix it with saliva. Saliva contains an enzyme (called amylase) that breaks down carbohydrates.

**Q3 a)** To kill harmful bacteria. To give a low pH for the stomach enzymes to work.

**b)** To move the stomach wall and churn up the food.

**Q4 a)** Liver. Makes bile to emulsify (break up) fats and give the right pH for the enzymes in the small intestine.

**b)** Pancreas. Makes enzymes (proteases, carbohydrases and lipases).

**c)** Small intestine. Where food is absorbed through the gut wall into the blood. Also makes more enzymes to further digest food.

**d)** Large intestine. Water is absorbed from here.

**e)** Rectum. Undigested food/faeces leaves the body from here (via the anus).

**Q5** Enzymes are biological **catalysts**. The body uses enzymes to **break up** big molecules into small ones. These smaller molecules can pass through the gut wall into the **blood**. From here they travel around the body, then pass into the **cells** to be used.

**Q6 a)** Pancreas and small intestine should be circled.

2

# Answers

b) carbohydrase, protease, lipase

c) The stomach

**Q7 a)** No, because there was no starch in the water outside the tubing after 25 minutes.

b) The molecules of glucose are small enough to pass through the tubing.

c) Both the dialysis tubing and the small intestine wall allow small (soluble) molecules to pass through them but not large (insoluble) molecules.

d) blood

e) (partly digested) food

**Q8 a)** small intestine

b) i) villi

ii) They have a thin outer layer of cells. They have a good blood supply. They provide a large surface area for absorption.

c) The molecules are carried from the gut to the body cells. They then diffuse out into cells to be used.

**Q9** Any two of, e.g. they produce enzymes that help to digest food. / They make useful vitamins (like vitamin K). / They produce useful hormones. / They reduce the possibility of harmful bacteria growing in your intestines and making you ill.

## Pages 21-22 — The Skeleton and Muscles

**Q1** The **bones** in your skeleton protect many important **organs** in your body. Bones also allow m**ovement** to occur at joints and they also **suppor**t the entire body.

**Q2 a)** B → D → C → A

b) backbone — spinal cord
skull — brain
ribs — heart and lungs

c) a joint

**Q3 a)** The outer layer of bone tissue is very strong and hard.

b) The inner layer of bone tissue is spongy but strong.

c) Bone marrow produces blood cells.

**Q4 a) i)** B
ii) C
iii) A
iv) D

b) Tendons attach muscles to bones.

c) Muscles are attached to bones. When a muscle contracts, it applies a force to the bone it's attached to, which makes the bone move.

## Pages 23-24 — How Muscles Work

**Q1 a)** Antagonistic muscles are pairs of muscles that work against each other.

b) i) triceps
ii) relaxed
iii) Muscle A/the triceps muscle will contract/shorten, pulling the arm straight. As this happens the biceps muscle will relax/lengthen.

**Q2 a)** A **pivot** is the point around which a rotation happens.

b) Your arm works as a **lever** with the elbow as a pivot. This means that when a force acts on your arm, a moment is created.

c) Moments are a measure of the **turning** effect of a force.

d) Moments are calculated using the formula:
Moment = **force × perpendicular distance**.

e) Moments are measured in **Nm**.

**Q3** Multiply the force by the perpendicular distance from the pivot.

**Q4 a)** Moment = force × perpendicular distance
= 5 × 0.24
= **1.2 Nm**

b) E.g. to counteract the moment of Roland's weight / to keep the arm still.

c) Force = moment ÷ perpendicular distance
= 1.2 ÷ 0.04
= **30 N**

## Pages 25-26 — Gas Exchange

**Q1** Lung — f
Trachea (wind pipe) — a
Bronchus — c
Bronchiole — e
Alveoli — g
Diaphragm — h
Rib — b
Intercostal muscle — d

**Q2** We need to take in **oxygen** from the **air** to stay alive. We also need to get rid of **carbon dioxide** from our bodies. This overall process is called **gas exchange**. The gas we take in enters our **blood** and is used with sugar in the cells to release **energy**.

**Q3 a) i)** oxygen

ii) Arrow drawn and labelled as shown below.

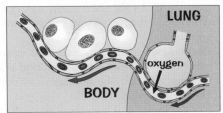

iii) Oxygen passes out of the bloodstream into the body cells where it is used in respiration.

b) i) carbon dioxide

ii) Arrow drawn and labelled as shown below.

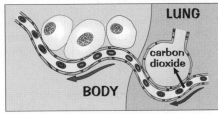

iii) It is a waste product of respiration.

c) diffusion

d) 1. They're moist.
2. They have a good blood supply.
3. The alveoli give the lungs a big inside surface area.

# Answers

## Pages 27-28 — Breathing

**Q1** a) lungs
b) trachea (windpipe)
c) bronchi (bronchus)
d) intercostal muscles and diaphragm muscle
e) diaphragm
f) chest cavity
g) i) They fill with air.
    ii) inhalation / breathing in

**Q2**
1. Rib muscles contract — Rib cage moves upwards and outwards
2. Diaphragm contracts — Diaphragm moves down and becomes flatter
3. More space is formed in the chest — Air enters to fill the extra room
4. Rib muscles relax — Rib cage moves downwards and inwards
5. Diaphragm relaxes — Diaphragm moves upwards
6. Less space is left in the chest — Air is forced out from the chest space

**Q3** a) The amount of air you can breathe into your lungs in a single breath.
b) Student B
c) 1.4 metres tall, because shorter people tend to have a smaller lung volume than taller people.

## Pages 29-30 — Exercise, Asthma and Smoking

**Q1** a) i) The rate of breathing and depth of breathing increase.
    ii) When you exercise, your muscles need more oxygen. Breathing deeper and faster allows you to get more oxygen into your blood.
b) It means that your chest cavity can open up more when you breathe, so you can get more air into your lungs.
c) Regular exercise can cause an increase in the number and size of the small blood vessels in your lungs and in the number of alveoli.

**Q2** a) They will contract.
b) E.g. the lining will become inflamed and fluid will build up, making it hard for him to breathe.
c) E.g. Difficulty breathing, wheezing, tight chest.
d) It contains drugs that open up the airways.

**Q3** true, false, true, true, false, true, false

**Q4** a) E.g. carbon monoxide, nicotine, particulates.
b) Tar **covers** the cilia on the lining of the airways. The damaged **cilia** can't get rid of **mucus** properly. The mucus **sticks** to the airways, which makes you **cough** more.
c) i) E.g. bronchitis and emphysema.
    ii) E.g. bronchitis inflames the lining of the bronchi. Emphysema destroys the alveoli (air sacs) in the lungs.

## Pages 31-33 — Human Reproductive Systems

**Q1**
A — urethra
B — scrotal sac/scrotum
C — testis
D — erectile tissue
E — foreskin
F — sperm duct
G — ovary
H — uterus/womb
I — vagina
J — cervix
K — fallopian tube/oviduct
b) sperm
c) To produce sperm.
d) semen
e) egg
f) To carry the egg from the ovary to the uterus.
g) It dies (and passes out of the vagina).

**Q2** An egg cell is released from an **ovary** once a **month**. Each time an egg cell is released the **uterus** gets ready to grow a baby. A thick lining full of **blood** vessels slowly develops. If the egg is **fertilised** it passes into the uterus and becomes attached to it. If the egg is not fertilised the breakdown of the uterus lining occurs. This is called **menstruation**. The whole sequence of making a new uterus lining and an egg is called the **menstrual cycle**.

**Q3** Ovary — The female organ which produces the egg
Uterus — The female organ which nurtures the fertilised egg
Menstruation — The breakdown of the uterus lining
Egg — The female sex cell
Menstrual cycle — The 4 week cycle of the female sex organs

**Q4** a)
1. D
2. B
3. C
4. D
5. A
b) (To give a good blood supply) in case it receives a fertilised egg.
c) 10 days
d) day 14

## Pages 34-36 — Having a Baby

**Q1** a)

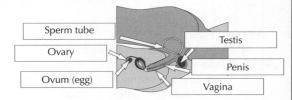

Sperm tube, Testis, Ovary, Penis, Ovum (egg), Vagina

b) sexual intercourse/copulation

**Q2** a) The nucleus of the egg must join with the nucleus of the sperm.
b) In the fallopian tube.
c) A zygote.
d) E.g. the egg divides from 1 cell into 32 cells.
e) The wall of the uterus / uterus lining.
f) About one week after fertilisation.

# Answers

**Q3**

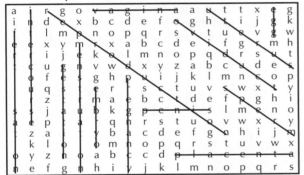

Mother's blood
Placenta
Umbilical cord
Foetus
Amniotic fluid

**Q4**
**a)** gestation/pregnancy
**b)** The embryo has a brain, heart, eyes and legs — 1 month.
It kicks and its finger nails can be felt — 5 months.
The foetus is viable — 7 months.
The baby is fully developed — 9 months.
**c)** At 9 weeks.
**d)** At 9 weeks.
**e)** The foetus would have a fair chance of surviving if it were born.

**Q5**
**a)** The placenta lets the blood of the foetus and mother get very close to allow exchange of food, oxygen and waste products.
**b) i)** Any two of, e.g. smoking, drinking alcohol, taking drugs.
**ii)** They get into the mother's blood, then they cross the placenta and can affect the foetus.
**iii)** It may not develop properly and could have health problems after it's born.

**Q6**

| a | i | r | g | o | v | a | g | i | n | a | a | a | t | t | x | e | g |
|---|---|---|---|---|---|---|---|---|---|---|---|---|---|---|---|---|---|
| i | n | d | e | x | b | c | d | e | f | o | g | h | i | j | k | g | k |
| f | e | l | m | y | n | o | p | q | r | s | v | t | u | e | v | g | w |
| e | e | x | i | j | e | k | x | a | b | c | d | e | i | f | g | r | m |
| t | c | u | f | j | k | o | l | m | n | o | p | q | d | r | s | u | h |
| o | u | f | j | g | m | v | w | d | x | y | z | a | b | c | u | d | t |
| u | f | q | z | h | r | g | h | p | u | i | j | k | l | m | n | e | s |
| s | q | z | m | r | a | k | g | i | s | t | u | v | w | x | g | h | p |
| a | e | j | a | u | b | k | g | p | e | n | i | s | l | m | e | n | i |
| t | e | p | a | l | q | b | h | r | s | t | u | o | v | w | x | r | o |
| z | a | l | z | h | b | m | a | c | d | e | f | g | n | h | i | j | y |
| k | l | o | n | o | a | b | m | n | o | p | q | r | s | t | u | v | m |
| o | y | l | z | h | o | a | b | c | d | p | l | a | c | e | n | t | x |
| n | e | f | g | m | h | i | j | j | k | l | m | n | o | p | q | r | s |

### Pages 37-39 — Health and Drugs
**Q1**
**a)** The absence of **disease**.
**b)** Eating a balanced **diet**.
**c)** Doing enough **exercise**.
**d)** Not abusing **drugs**.

**Q2**
**a)** Growth — getting to adult size
Nutrition — getting food to stay alive
Respiration — turning food into energy
Excretion — getting rid of waste
Movement — moving parts of the body
Sensitivity — responding and reacting
Reproduction — producing offspring
**b)** excretion/nutrition
**c)** movement and sensitivity

**Q3**
**a)** Any substance that affects the way the body works.
**b)** They're used for enjoyment, rather than as medicine.

**Q4**
**a)** 4
**b)** 1
**c)** 2
**d)** 3

**Q5**
**a)** depressant
**b)** brain and liver
**c)** It slows down responses so accidents can't be avoided in time and it impairs judgement which can lead to accidents.

**Q6** Anything that makes you want more of it.

**Q7**
**a)** E.g. paints, aerosols and glue.
**b) i)** Gives hallucinations
Affects your behaviour
**ii)** Can damage the lungs
Can damage the brain

**Q8**

DRUG CONTAINER

ORGAN DAMAGED

### Section 3 — Plants and Ecosystems
### Pages 40-44 — Plant Nutrition
**Q1**
**a)** carbon dioxide + water → glucose + oxygen
**b) i)** carbon dioxide and water
**ii)** glucose and oxygen
**c)** carbohydrate

**Q2**
1. (sun)light
2. chlorophyll
3. water
4. carbon dioxide

**Q3**
**a)** carbon dioxide
**b)** oxygen

**Q4**

Crossword:
1. carbon
2. oxy(gen)
3. soil
4. light
5. glucose
6. mi...
7. d(ioxide)
8. photosynthesis
9. leaf
10. ...
11. water
12. dark
13. green

**Q5**
**a)** The soil.
**b)** The roots.

**Q6**
**a)** Both plants were watered regularly.
**b)** E.g. you could repeat the experiment several times with other plants.
**c) i)** E.g. the plant will die / shrivel up / lose leaves.
**ii)** They need light and water to survive.

**Q7**
**a) i)** Potassium.
**ii)** Leaves become yellow with dead spots.
**b)** Phosphate. The roots didn't grow properly in beaker C, which is missing phosphate.
**c)** Yellowing of leaves and weakening of the stem.
**d)** E.g. the plants would eventually die / would be unhealthy / would be yellow and weak.

# Answers

**Q8** **a)** Gives the leaf a big surface area for absorbing light.

**b)** Means that as much light as possible reaches the chloroplasts.

**c)** The veins deliver water to the leaf cells and take away glucose.

**d)** Allows carbon dioxide to diffuse in and oxygen to diffuse out easily.

**Q9** Photosynthesis requires carbon dioxide.

**Q10 a)** Plant A — e.g. would be normal and healthy.
Plant B — e.g. would be unhealthy/dead.

**b)** Plants take in carbon dioxide and release oxygen through the stomata, which are found on the underside of the leaf. If these are covered in Vaseline®, the plant can't photosynthesise, so it will start to die.

**Q11 a)** oxygen

**b)** Plants produce oxygen during photosynthesis, so the bubbles will be oxygen gas.

## Pages 45-48 — Plant Reproduction

**Q1** The **male** sex cell is produced by the pollen, and the **female** sex cell is contained in the **ovule**.

**Q2** **a) i), b) i) and c) i)**

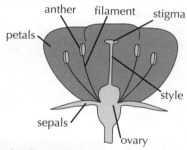

**ii)** The filament supports the anther.
**iii)** The anther contains the pollen grains, which produce the male sex cells.
**b) ii)** The carpel.
**iii)** The ovules / female sex cells.
**c) ii)** The main difference is colour, as petals are usually brightly coloured but sepals are green.
**iii)** They protect the budding flower.
**iv)** They attract insects.

**Q3** The female sex cell in plants is contained inside — the ovule.
The female sex organ in plants is called — the carpel.
The female sex organ is made up from — the stigma, style and ovary.
The male sex cell in plants is produced by — the pollen.
The male sex organ in plants is called — the stamen.
The male sex organ is made up from — the filament and anther.

**Q4** insect-pollinated — buttercup, daisy, sunflower
wind-pollinated — grass, stinging nettle, willow tree

**Q5** The extra words to find are: stamen, carpel

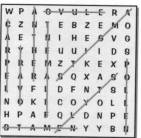

**Q6** **a)** The travel of pollen from a stamen to a stigma.
**b) i)** B
**ii)** E.g. it has feathery stigmas (and long anthers) that hang outside the flower. It has dull/green petals.
**c) i)** A
**ii)** E.g. it has large, brightly coloured petals. It has a stigma (and anthers) that are inside the flower.
**d)** Lighter pollen is more easily carried by the wind.
**e)**

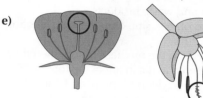

**f)** Insect pollinated plants have sticky stigmas to take the pollen off the insect. Wind pollinated plants have feathery stigmas to catch pollen as it's carried past in the wind.

**Q7** **a)** Wind pollinated, because insect pollinated plants are scented to attract insects.
**b)** They will be small and dull.
**c) i)** Glands that produce nectar/a sugary liquid for insects to feed on.
**ii)** no

**Q8** **a) i)** one
**ii)** two
**b)** These statements should be circled:
Some plants only have male flowers, and others only have female flowers.
The stamens and carpels of the flowers mature at different times.

## Pages 49-50 — Fertilisation and Seed Formation

**Q1** **a)** style
**b)** fertilisation
**c)** ovary
**d) i)** a food store
**ii)** When the seed germinates/starts to grow.
**e)** They are spread out/carried away from the parent plant.

**Q2** release of pollen → pollination → growth of pollen tube → fertilisation → seed production dispersal → germination → growth of seedling

**Q3** **a)** Dandelion: has parachutes on its seeds to help them catch the wind.
Sycamore: has wings to help it fly away from the parent tree.
**b)** The animal will disperse the seeds in its droppings.

c) Tomato: bright red skin attracts an animal, who eats it and spreads the seeds via droppings. Burdock: hooks catch on animal's fur/coat, so it gets carried away.

d) E.g. apple (accept any sensible fruit). It is attractive because of its colour/smell/taste.

## Pages 51-52 — Investigating Seed Dispersal Mechanisms

**Q1** a) E.g. the person dropping the fruit, the height the fruits are dropped from and the place where the experiment takes place.

b) The type of fruit.

c) E.g. a tape measure / ruler.

d) To increase the reliability of the experiment. / If she did it just once she could get an anomalous result.

e) i) Sycamore = (20 + 25 + 21) ÷ 3 = **22 cm**

ii) Elm = (18 + 14 + 16) ÷ 3 = **16 cm**

f) E.g. sycamore fruits disperse further than elm fruits.

**Q2** a) 0 cm: (6 + 10 + 5) ÷ 3 = **7 cm**
1 cm: (9 + 7 + 11) ÷ 3 = **9 cm**
2 cm: (15 + 17 + 19) ÷ 3 = **17 cm**
3 cm: (26 + 24 + 25) ÷ 3 = **25 cm**
4 cm: (30 + 33 + 27) ÷ 3 = **30 cm**

b) Graph to show how fruit wing length affects dispersal

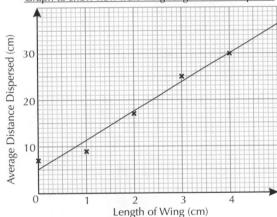

c) 30 cm – 7 cm = **23 cm**

d) The longer the wings on a sycamore fruit, the further the fruit will disperse.

## Pages 53-54 — Dependence on Other Organisms

**Q1** a) the Sun

b) Plants use the Sun's energy to make food during photosynthesis.

c) E.g. only plants can use photosynthesis to capture and store the Sun's energy. Other living things need plants to do this so they can then eat them and get the energy they need to live.

**Q2** a) bacterium, bird, dandelion, dog, fish, frog, seaweed, snake

b) oxygen

c) carbon dioxide

d) oxygen

e) Photosynthesis helps make sure there's always plenty of oxygen around for respiration.

**Q3** a) An ecosystem is all the living organisms in one area, plus their environment.

b) They need each other to survive.

**Q4** a) Many plants depend on insects to pollinate them. Without the insects the plants would struggle to reproduce.

b) E.g. we need insects to pollinate crop plants, so they can produce fruit. If insect numbers fall, fewer plants may be pollinated, so less fruit may be produced.

c) E.g. we may have less food available. This could lead to increased food prices, food shortages, or even famine.

## Pages 55-58 — Food Chains and Food Webs

**Q1** carnivores — animals that eat other animals
omnivores — animals that eat both plants and animals
herbivores — animals that eat plants
consumers — organisms that rely on other organisms for their food
producers — organisms that can make their own food

**Q2** a) They show what is eaten by/is food for what. / how energy flows through the food chain.

b) i) herbivore: limpet
carnivore: lobster
producer: algae

ii) The algae are the start of the food chain so they must be the producer. The limpet eats algae so must be a herbivore. The lobster eats limpets, so must be a carnivore.

**Q3** a) plant/producer

b) They can produce their own food by photosynthesis.

**Q4** The words to find are: carnivore, consumer, food chain, omnivore, producer, herbivore

| E | P | C | O | N | S | U | M | E | R |
|---|---|---|---|---|---|---|---|---|---|
| R | R | F | O | I | D | C | H | A | O |
| O | E | O | O | A | E | R | B | M | I |
| V | C | O | M | H | I | V | N | C | A |
| I | U | D | A | C | H | I | N | G | R |
| B | D | C | E | D | V | O | R | E | S |
| R | O | H | S | O | K | I | Z | X | L |
| E | R | A | R | O | A | R | N | I | V |
| H | P | E | R | F | V | I | B | R | A |
| X | E | R | O | V | I | N | R | A | C |

**Q5** a) An animal that eats producers — grasshopper.

b) An animal that eats primary consumers — snake.

c) An animal that eats secondary consumers — hawk.

d) An animal that is not eaten by anything else — hawk.

**Q6** a) i) Blue tit, hawk, owl and fox should be circled.

ii) blue tit

b) blackberry — aphid — blue tit — hawk
blackberry — caterpillar — blue tit — hawk
blackberry — mouse — hawk

c) blackberry — mouse — owl

d) The number of voles might increase because they have more food.

e) i) There would be more blue tits because less would be eaten.

# Answers

ii) There would be fewer aphids because there would be more blue tits eating them.

**Q7** false, false, true, false, true, false, true

**Q8** a) Weasels, foxes and hawks.

b) The organisms at the top of the food chain/top carnivores are worst affected because the poisons build up as they are passed along the food chain.

c) hawk

## Section 4 — Inheritance, Variation and Survival

### Pages 59-60 — DNA and Inheritance

**Q1** a) A — Nucleus
B — Chromosome
C — Cell
D — Gene
E — DNA

b)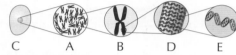
C    A    B    D    E

**Q2** a) B should be crossed.

b) Genes normally work in pairs.

**Q3** a) They fuse together.

b) i) 46

ii) 23

iii) 23

iv) 23

v) 1, 1

c) E.g. during reproduction, the fertilised egg gets one copy of each gene from the mother and one from the father. Genes control characteristics so this means the offspring will have a mixture of their parents' characteristics.

d) heredity

**Q4** a) E.g. X-ray data

b) A spiral made of two chains wound together.

### Pages 61-63 — Variation

**Q1** a) Natasha looks different from the seal because they are **different** species.

b) They have different genes.

c) Variation can happen within a **species**. That means that plants and **animals** that have basically the same **genes** will still show differences between them. For example, human beings have different skin colours. These **differences** are known as characteristic features.

d) Inherited — These features come from your parents via genes.
Environmental — These features are caused by your surroundings.

e) Natasha's eye colour — Inherited
Natasha's tattoo — Environmental
Rodney's haircut — Environmental

**Q2** a)

| Eye Colour | Tally | Number of children |
|---|---|---|
| Brown | HＩＩＩＩ | 9 |
| Blue | H H ＩＩ | 12 |
| Green | H | 5 |
| Hazel | HＩ | 6 |

b)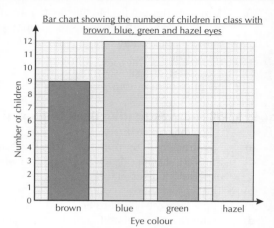

Bar chart showing the number of children in class with brown, blue, green and hazel eyes

c) Total number of children = 9 + 12 + 5 + 6 = 32
Percentage with blue eyes = (12 ÷ 32) × 100
= **37.5%**

d) Discontinuous variation, because eye colour can only take certain values/falls into distinct categories, not a continuous range.

**Q3** a)

| Height (cm) | Frequency |
|---|---|
| $134 < h \leq 139$ | 1 |
| $139 < h \leq 144$ | 3 |
| $144 < h \leq 149$ | 6 |
| $149 < h \leq 154$ | 8 |
| $154 < h \leq 159$ | 7 |
| $159 < h \leq 164$ | 4 |
| $164 < h \leq 169$ | 1 |

b)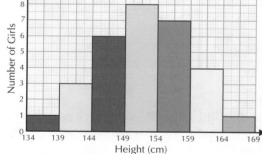

Bar chart showing the heights of girls in two year 7 classes

c) i) Taller than 159 cm

ii) No taller than 149 cm

d) Any three from e.g. weight, skin colour, intelligence, leaf area.

### Pages 64-66 — Natural Selection and Survival

**Q1** a) i) B. It has bigger claws than A, and twice as many claws as C. So lobster B will be better than A and C at catching food and defending itself.

ii) Lobster C

b) In a population of lobsters the individuals which are most like **lobster B** would be more likely to survive. This means that they are more likely to **reproduce** and pass their **genes** on to their young. Gradually the whole population would become more and more like **lobster B**.

c) Natural selection

# Answers

**Q2** **a)** E.g. slow rabbits are easier to catch by foxes and so not many of them get the chance to reproduce and pass on their genes.

**b)** E.g. fast rabbits are more likely to escape the foxes and so have more chance of reproducing successfully and passing on their genes.

**c)** E.g. the fast rabbits are more likely to breed and pass on their genes to their offspring, which inherit the genes for running fast.

**d)** E.g. the rabbit from the field with foxes is more likely to win. In the field with foxes fast rabbits are more likely to survive and pass on their genes, while slow rabbits are more likely to be eaten before they can reproduce. So being fast becomes more common. In the field without foxes, slow rabbits are as likely to survive as fast rabbits and don't die out. So rabbits from the field without foxes are more likely to be slow.

**Q3** **a)** These should be circled: Other species that eat seals, other polar bears.

**b) i)** genes

**ii)** E.g. the ice was thicker, so polar bears with weak limbs couldn't break the ice to get seals underneath, so they had nothing to eat and died.

**Q4** D, E, A, C, B

## Pages 67-68 — Extinction and Preserving Species

**Q1** **a)** Gorillas **survive** in rainforests because they are well adapted to **compete** for food in that environment. When the trees in the rainforest are cut down to make room for fields, there is less **food** for the gorillas to eat. Those gorillas that are less able to compete successfully for food will **struggle** to survive and **reproduce**.

**b) i)** Extinct — None of that species are left.

**ii)** Endangered — At risk of becoming extinct.

**Q2** **a)** Accept any two things humans use that we obtain from plants or animals.
For example: clothing/fabric/wool, medicine (or an example of a named medicine), fuel/wood, building materials/wood.

**b)** You must give two examples that match your answers from part a). For example:
Item 1 (wool): Organism — sheep. Effect on humans — if sheep became extinct, we would need to find other materials to make warm clothes from.
Item 2 (wood): Organism — pine tree. Effect on humans — if pine trees became extinct, we would have to use more man-made building materials/cut down more of other types of tree.

**Q3** **a)** genes

**b)** biodiversity

**Q4** **a)** sperm, eggs

**b)** They must be frozen.

**c)** E.g. use the stored egg and sperm cells to create new animal embryos.

**d)** Stop species becoming extinct in the first place, by e.g. preventing the destruction of habitats.

**Q5** E.g. the organisms could be sources of useful products which humans cannot make use of if the species becomes extinct. / Because the rainforest

is a complex ecosystem, the loss of some species could have knock-on effects for other species, including humans.

# Chemistry
## Section 1 — Classifying Materials
### Page 1 — Solids, Liquids and Gases

**Q1**
1. Particles
2. Compressing
3. Properties
4. Solid
5. Three
6. Volume
7. Liquids
8. Gas

**Q2** **a)** Solid

**b)** Gas

**c)** Liquid

### Pages 2-5 — Particle Theory

**Q1** **a)** T

**b)** F

**c)** F

**d)** T

**e)** T

**f)** T

**g)** T

**Q2**

| | Particles are close together | Particles are held in fixed positions | Particles are moving or vibrating |
|---|---|---|---|
| **Solid** | ✔ | ✔ | ✔ |
| **Liquid** | ✔ | | ✔ |
| **Gas** | | | ✔ |

**Q3** A — X, B — Z, C —Y

**Q4** E.g. the forces between particles in solids are very strong, they hold the particles very close together and stop the particles being able to move much. In liquids the forces between the particles are slightly weaker. The particles are held close together, but they can move past each other. In gases the forces between particles are very weak, so the particles are far apart.

**Q5** **a)** Yes

**b)** No

**Q6** **a)** E.g. particles are close together but able to move past each other. They're constantly moving in all directions.

**b)** E.g. constant volume, ability to flow, not easily compressed.

**Q7** In a solid, the particles are held very **closely** together in **fixed** positions, although they do **vibrate** to and fro a little. The particles don't **move** from their positions, so all solids keep a **fixed** shape and **volume** and can't **flow** like liquids. Solids can't easily be **compressed** because the particles are already packed very **closely** together. Solids are usually **dense** as there are lots of particles in a **small** volume.

**Q8** The following should be ticked:
Particles move fast.
Particles collide with the container.
No definite shape.
Very low density.

# Answers

**Q9** E.g. the pressure will increase. When the temperature is increased, the particles move faster. This means that they hit the walls of the container harder and more often. Both of these things increase the pressure.

**Q10** E.g. if you reduce the volume of a gas the pressure increases. This is because when the particles are squashed up into a smaller space they'll hit the walls more often.

**Q11 a)** E.g. the particles want to spread out. They move from an area of high concentration (near the bucket) to an area of low concentration (the next room).

**b)** E.g. he is wrong. Diffusion is slow because the particles from whatever is making a smell keep bumping into air particles. This stops them moving forward and sends them off in different directions.

## Pages 6-8 — Physical Changes

**Q1 a)** A — Melting     D — Condensing
B — Freezing     E — Subliming
C — Boiling

**b)** E.g. the particles gain energy when a liquid is heated. They move faster, which weakens the forces holding the liquid together. At a certain temperature the particles have enough energy to break the forces and the liquid becomes a gas.

**c) i)** When the state changes, the energy of the particles changes.

**ii)** A change of state doesn't involve a change in mass.

**iii)** E.g. condensing is the opposite of boiling / freezing is the opposite of melting.

**Q2** Solid. E.g. the particles in a solid have very strong forces between them that need to be broken for it to form a gas.

**Q3** E.g. the particles gain energy and vibrate more. This weakens the forces holding the solid together and allows the distance between the particles to increase.

**Q4**

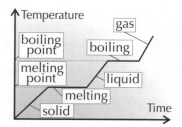

**Q5 a) i)** A — Gas
C — Liquid
E — Solid

**ii)** B — Condensing
D — Freezing

**b)** E.g. the graph is flat at B and D because forces between particles get stronger when a gas condenses and when a liquid freezes. Energy is given out when forces between particles get stronger, so the temperature doesn't start to go down again until all the water has changed state.

## Pages 9-13 — Atoms and Elements

**Q1** Atoms are really tiny, so you can't see them directly.

**Q2** Dalton was the first scientist to try and explain things about **atoms**. He said that all **matter** was made up of atoms. He also said that there were **different** kinds of atom, and that each **element** contained a different type of atom.

**Q3 a)** agree
**b)** disagree
**c)** agree
**d)** agree
**e)** agree
**f)** disagree
**g)** disagree

**Q4** These should be ticked: carbon, nitrogen, uranium, helium.

**Q5**

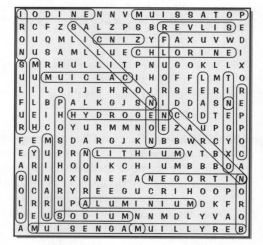

**Q6 a)** carbon
**b)** chlorine
**c)** calcium
**d)** copper
**e)** sodium
**f)** fluorine

**Q7** carbon, hydrogen, oxygen, phosphorus, potassium, iodine, nitrogen, sulfur, calcium, iron.

**Q8** A — hydrogen     D — argon
B — helium     E — oxygen
C — chlorine     F — iodine

**Q9** Pupils who work hard will do well.

**Q10** I love homework. More for me.

**Q11** E.g. Beryllium, sulfur, (thorium-hydrogen) / (dysprosium-yttrium), oxygen / sulfur, oxygen, (manganese-nitrogen), (europium-uranium) / tungsten, oxygen, (rubidium-boron), potassium / (molybdenum-oxygen), astatine, (einsteinium-sulfur), yttrium!

**Q12** Depends on your message.

## Pages 14-15 — The Periodic Table

**Q1 a)** elements
**b)** A column of elements.

# Answers

c)

E.g. Group 0 or 8 = noble gases

d) A row of elements.

e) Metals are to the left, non-metals are to the right.

**Q2** a) Silicon is a non-metal.

b) Chlorine is a non-metal.

c) Oxygen as all the others are Group 7 elements.

d) Hydrogen is not a noble gas.

e) Fe as it is not in Group 1.

f) Lithium is the only metal.

**Q3** a) The first sentence should be crossed.

b) The groups in the periodic table contain elements that have very similar properties.

**Q4** a) Group 7, very reactive

b) Group 0, very unreactive

c) Group 2, very reactive

**Q5** a) Group 1

b) The elements get more reactive as you go down the group.

c) It caught fire — potassium
It fizzed a lot — sodium
It fizzed a bit — lithium

d) It would explode.

## Pages 16-17 — Compounds

**Q1** Elements are made up of only one type of atom. Compounds have atoms of different elements joined together.

**Q2** Elements — sulfur, lead, oxygen, helium, calcium, chlorine
Compounds — magnesium oxide, sodium chloride, water, carbon dioxide, sulfur dioxide, carbon monoxide, sulfuric acid

**Q3** sodium chloride — sodium and chlorine
carbon dioxide — carbon and oxygen
water — hydrogen, oxygen

**Q4** a) A

b) Two different types of atom are joined/bonded together.

c) B and C

d) In C, the element is made up of atoms.
In B, the element is made up of molecules.

e) D

**Q5** a) $Fe + S \rightarrow FeS$

b) Products — iron sulfide
Reactants — iron, sulfur

c) E.g. The new compounds made/produced in a chemical reaction are totally different from the original elements. You can't say if iron bromide is magnetic or not without testing it.

## Pages 18-19 — Naming Compounds

**Q1** a) elements, ide

b) combine, oxygen, ate

c) E.g. copper sulphate, zinc carbonate.

**Q2** water — $H_2O$
iron oxide — $Fe_2O_3$
carbon dioxide — $CO_2$
calcium carbonate — $CaCO_3$
silver nitrate — $AgNO_3$
carbon monoxide — $CO$
sodium chloride — $NaCl$

**Q3** a) Fluorine, $F_2$

b) A molecule made up of two identical atoms (i.e. of the same element) is an element.

c) Any two of e.g. hydrogen, oxygen, nitrogen, chlorine

**Q4** a) sodium chloride

b) sodium bromide

c) sodium oxide

**Q5** a) calcium Ca, carbon C, oxygen O

b) calcium Ca, oxygen O

c) lithium Li, bromine Br

d) copper Cu, sulfur S, oxygen O

**Q6** a) hydrogen chloride / hydrochloric acid

b) oxygen

c) nitrogen

d) magnesium oxide

e) iron chloride

f) copper sulfate

**Q7** a) HCl

b) $O_2$

c) $N_2$

d) MgO

e) $FeCl_3$

f) $CuSO_4$

## Pages 20-22 — Mixtures

**Q1** pen ink — M, water — C, air — M, carbon dioxide — C, a cup of tea — M, pure salt — C, concrete — M, crude oil — M, bromine — E, rust — C, sugar — C, magnesium — E

**Q2** E.g. a substance made up of only one type of element or only one type of compound.

**Q3** a) A and C

b) C

c) Sample A — Water
Sample B — Air
Sample C — Xenon

**Q4** a) E.g. two or more substances that aren't chemically joined up.

b) The mixture, because it can be separated using physical methods. Compounds can only be separated into elements by a chemical reaction.

**Q5** a) Solute

b) Solvent

c) Solution

d) Soluble

e) Insoluble

f) Saturated

g) Solubility

**Q6** a) A solution in which no more solute will dissolve.

b) E.g. the bonds holding the sodium chloride together will break and the particles will mix with the water particles, making a solution.

# Answers

**Q7 a)** Before sugar is added:

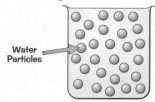

Water Particles

After the sugar is added:

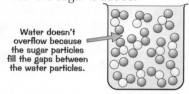

Water doesn't overflow because the sugar particles fill the gaps between the water particles.

**b)** 84 g. No mass is lost when something dissolves.

**Q8 a) i)** Solubility increases with temperature.

**ii)** More solute dissolves in water as the temperature increases because the particles are moving faster.

**b)** Sodium nitrate

**c)** Some solutes won't dissolve in certain solvents, so she can't say for sure without doing the experiment.

## Pages 23-26 — Separating Mixtures

**Q1** Salt solution — E
Crude oil — D
Coffee — E
Sugar solution — E
Muddy water — F and E

**Q2** E.g. make sure the lawn sand is a fine powder — if there are big lumps, grind them up with a mortar and pestle. Fertiliser is soluble and sand isn't, so filtration and evaporation can be used to separate the two. Weigh a sample of lawn sand and a piece of filter paper separately. Mix the sample with water in a beaker so that the fertiliser dissolves. Filter the contents of the beaker using filter paper and a funnel — the sand particles are too big to pass through the filter paper but the fertiliser is dissolved in the water and will pass through. Wash the sand left in the filter paper with more water to remove all fertiliser. Dry the sand and filter paper, and weigh them. Subtract the weight of the filter paper to find the weight of the sand. If it's half the weight of the original sample, then the other half must have been fertiliser and she hasn't been cheated.

**Q3 a)** simple distillation

**b)** The water is a gas, so it must be cooled and condensed into a liquid so it can be collected.

**c)** The water in the ink boils off, cools and is collected in the beaker.

**d)** E.g. sea water

**Q4 a)**

Ink spot

Wick

Solvent

Filter paper

Different dyes in the ink

**b)** E.g. the solvent soaks through the paper because of the wick. Different dyes in the ink are washed through the paper by the solvent at different rates. Some dyes in the ink will stick to the paper and others will dissolve in the solvent. The dyes stop at different points, forming different-sized rings.

**Q5 a)** 2

**b)** Paul

**c)** Paul's ink and the note ink were both made up of two dyes and the results show these dyes travelled the same amount along the filter paper — they're probably the same ink.

**Q6 a)** Coolest bit of the column — B
Condenser — F
Hottest part of column — D
0-400 °C Thermometer — A
Fractionating column — C
Collected fractions — G
Crude oil — E

**b)** Different liquids boil off at different temperatures around their own boiling point. The fractionating column ensures that the "wrong" liquids condense back down, and only the liquid boiling at the temperature on the thermometer will make it to the top and be collected. When each liquid has boiled off, the temperature reading rises until the next fraction starts to boil off.

**Q7 a)** To check the purity of the water. Pure chemical substances have fixed melting and boiling points.

**b)** The water was pure.

**c)** The water contained impurities that caused it to boil above the normal boiling point and freeze below the normal freezing point.

## Pages 27-29 — Properties of Metals

**Q1** All the elements to the left of the zigzag should be shaded.

**Q2 a)** When particles are heated they start to vibrate strongly. This is passed on through the metal.

**b)** E.g. malleable, high melting point, strong and tough.

**c) i)** A negatively-charged particle.

**ii)** Because electrical charges can move through them easily.

**iii)** Moving charges.

**Q3 a)** An alloy

**b)** By themselves, neither **tin** nor **lead** would be very useful for joining circuits together. Lead melts at a relatively **low** temperature, but it's not very good at conducting **electricity**. On the other hand, tin is a **good** conductor of electricity, but it **can't** easily be melted. When they're **mixed** together, the properties get mixed up, and you end up with an **alloy** that melts at a low temperature and conducts electricity.

**Q4 a)** Metals have a high tensile strength because of the strong bonds between the metal particles.

**b)** Metals look shiny when polished because light reflects strongly from the surface.

**c)** The atoms in metals are joined with very strong

# Answers

**Q5** These should be circled: a 2p coin, cobalt, nickel, Sir Galahad's suit of steel armor.

**Q6 a)** The atoms in metals can slide over each other.
   **b)** Metals are ductile.

**Q7 a) i)** This sentence should be ticked.
   **ii)** This sentence should be crossed.
   **b)** Metals have high densities because they have lots of particles in a small space.

## Pages 30-32 — Properties of Non-Metals

**Q1**

| B | C | N | O | F | Ne |
|---|---|---|---|---|----|
| Al | Si | P | S | Cl | Ar |
| Ga | Ge | As | Se | Br | Kr |
| In | Sn | Sb | Te | I | Xe |
| Tl | Pb | Bi | Po | At | Rn |

**Q2 a)** They are at low temperatures.
   **b)** The densities of non-metals tends to be lower than those of metals.

**Q3** The steel barrel could be lifted out.

**Q4** The forces between the particles in a non-metal are weak. This means they break apart easily.

**Q5** 1 — Non-metal
   2 — Metal
   3 — Non-metal

**Q6 a)** carbon
   **b)** It breaks.
   **c)** Non-metals are brittle.
   **d)** Unlike all other non-metals, graphite conducts electricity. This is because the atoms are arranged in layers. Electrons can move along the layers, which means graphite can conduct electricity.

**Q7 a)** non-metal
   **b)** A — The bulb doesn't light. Non-metals don't conduct electricity because electrons can't flow through them.
   B — Substance Q cracks. Non-metals are brittle because their particles are held together by weak forces.
   C — Substance Q melts in a bunsen flame. Non-metals have low-melting points because their particles are held together by weak forces.
   C — John's fingers don't get burned because non-metals transfer energy between thermal energy stores poorly.
   D — Substance Q isn't attracted to a magnet. Non-metals are not magnetic.

## Pages 33-35 — Properties of Other Materials

**Q1** Things made of ceramic — Any three from e.g. brakes, spark plugs, cups and mugs.
   Things made of polymers — Any three from e.g. crash helmets, kayaks, carrier bags, drinks bottles.

**Q2** Ceramic — Any two from e.g. thermal insulators, insulators of electricity, stiff.
   Polymer — Any two from e.g. thermal insulators, insulators of electricity, flexible, low density, easily moulded.

**Q3** Depends on your choices. E.g. brake pads are made from ceramic because they can withstand strong forces and they are thermal insulators.

**Q4** A polymer. Polymers are thermal insulators, so you won't burn your hands. They are also light for their size, so the kettle will be easy to carry. Polymers can be easily moulded into the shape of a kettle.

**Q5** China cup — C     Porcelain toilet — C
   Brick — C     Bin liner — P
   Milk bottle — P     Rubber duck — P

**Q6** Because they are good thermal insulators.

**Q7 a)** A material made from two or more different materials stuck together.
   **b)** It is stronger than plastic alone and less brittle than glass alone.
   **c)** E.g. skis, surfboards.

**Q8** It is a thermal insulator, so it takes a while to get hot. It is also brittle, so it can break easily.

**Q9 a)** A composite material.
   **b)** Sand, gravel and cement should be ticked.
   **c)** It can withstand being squashed (high compression stress), so it's good at supporting heavy things.

**Q10 a)** Polymers — polymers have lower densities than metals, but are still very strong. This means planes made from polymers will be lighter (and need less fuel to get off the ground).
   **b)** Polymers can be easily moulded.

## Section 2 — Chemical Changes
### Page 36 — Chemical Reactions

**Q1 a)** True
   **b)** True
   **c)** False
   **d)** False
   **e)** True

**Q2 a)** The reaction gives out energy.
   **b)** Muhammad is wrong — the total mass of a reaction mixture doesn't change during a reaction. Atoms are not created or destroyed in a reaction.

## Pages 37-39 — Examples of Chemical Reactions

**Q1 a) i)** $25.00 - 24.65 = \mathbf{0.35}$ **g**
   **ii)** It decreased. When the copper carbonate is heated it forms carbon dioxide (as well as copper oxide). The carbon dioxide formed is a gas and escapes from the test tube.
   **b)** copper carbonate $\rightarrow$ copper oxide + carbon dioxide
   **c)** thermal decomposition

**Q2 a)** Oxidation is when a substance reacts and combines with oxygen.
   **b)** Combustion should be circled.

**Q3 a)** It had rusted.
   **b) i)** $50.47 - 50.10 = \mathbf{0.37}$ **g**
   **ii)** increase

# Answers

iii) The nail has had oxygen added to it through the rusting process, which has increased its weight.
c) iron + oxygen → iron oxide
d) oxidation/rusting
e) The air.
f) orange/brown
Q4 a) combustion
b) by light and by heating
c) Yes (because $CO_2$ is released by the reaction).
Q5 a) Fuel, heating and oxygen.
b) hydrocarbon + oxygen → carbon dioxide + water (+ energy)
c) A bonfire

## Pages 40-41 — More on Chemical Reactions
Q1 a) True
b) False
c) True
d) False
e) True
Q2 a) It is exothermic / it gives out energy to the surroundings.
b) E.g. neutralisation/combustion reactions.
Q3 a) A catalyst is a substance which speeds up a chemical reaction without being changed or used up in the reaction itself.
b) They lower the minimum amount of energy / the temperature a reaction can happen at. They can also speed up a reaction.
c) Yes, catalysts don't get used up or changed in a reaction.
d) They increase the amount of product made in a given time. They make the industrial reaction cheaper (by lowering the minimum temperature the reaction can happen at).
e) E.g. Catalysts are expensive and different reactions use different catalysts so you can't just buy one catalyst to use for all reactions. Catalysts also need to be cleaned and they can be poisoned by impurities.
Q4 a) catalyst
b) thermal
c) decrease
d) endothermic
e) changed
f) exothermic
The mystery word is change.

## Pages 42-44 — Balancing Equations
Q1 b) 1 copper (Cu), 1 sulfur (S), 4 oxygen (O)
c) 1 sodium (Na), 1 chlorine (Cl)
d) 2 iron (Fe), 3 oxygen (O)
e) 1 nitrogen (N), 3 hydrogen (H)
f) 2 hydrogen (H), 1 oxygen (O)
g) 1 copper (Cu), 1 oxygen (O)
Q2 a) aluminium oxide
b) magnesium oxide
c) sodium chloride
Q3 a) How many of each chemical react or are made in a reaction.
b) calcium + oxygen → calcium oxide
c) Ca (calcium), $O_2$ (oxygen)

d) $2Ca + O_2 \rightarrow 2CaO$
Q4 $Na + 2HCl \rightarrow NaCl + H_2$ and $Al + Cl_2 \rightarrow AlCl$ are unbalanced.
Q5 a)

| Element | Number of atoms | |
| | Left side of the equation | Right side of the equation |
| --- | --- | --- |
| Fe | 2 | 1 |
| O | 3 | 2 |
| C | 1 | 1 |

b) $2Fe_2O_3 + C \rightarrow Fe + 3CO_2$
c) $2Fe_2O_3 + 3C \rightarrow 4Fe + 3CO_2$
Q6 a) $2Ba + O_2 \rightarrow 2BaO$
b) $2HCl + Mg \rightarrow MgCl_2 + H_2$
c) $2HCl + CuO \rightarrow CuCl_2 + H_2O$
d) $4Fe + 3O_2 \rightarrow 2Fe_2O_3$
Q7 a) This equation is correctly balanced.
b) $Ca + 2HCl \rightarrow CaCl_2 + H_2$
c) $CH_4 + 2O_2 \rightarrow CO_2 + 2H_2O$
d) $2ZnO + C \rightarrow 2Zn + CO_2$
e) This equation is correctly balanced.
f) $2C_2H_6 + 7O_2 \rightarrow 4CO_2 + 6H_2O$
g) This equation is correctly balanced.

## Pages 45-46 — Acids and Alkalis
Q1 Apple — acid
Orange — acid
Lemonade — acid
Bleach — alkali
Water — neutral
Washing powder — alkali
Q2
pH Scale
| 0 | 1 | 2 | 3 | 4 | 5 | 6 | 7 | 8 | 9 | 10 | 11 | 12 | 13 | 14 |
i) ii) iii) v) iv)
Q3

| Useful Substance | pH value | Colour with Universal Indicator | Acid, Alkaline or Neutral |
| --- | --- | --- | --- |
| a) Hydrochloric acid in stomach | pH1 | red | strong acid |
| b) Rain water | pH6 | yellow | weak acid |
| c) Sodium hydroxide | pH13 | purple | strong alkali |
| d) Tap water | pH7 | green | neutral |
| e) Washing up liquid | pH8 | blue | weak alkali |

Q4 a) i) E.g. litmus
ii) E.g. red (answer will depend on answer to a)i))
iii) E.g. blue (answer will depend on answer to a)i))
b) Universal indicator gives you the strength/pH of the acid or alkali.
Q5 a) Take a small sample of the acid and alkali and test them separately with a few drops of the indicator.
b) i) acidic
ii) green

## Pages 47-49 — Neutralisation Reactions
Q1 a) neutralisation
b) pH 7

# Answers

c) i) Sodium hydroxide + **sulfuric acid** → sodium sulfate + water

ii) Sodium hydroxide + **nitric acid** → sodium nitrate + water

iii) Calcium hydroxide + **hydrochloric acid** → calcium chloride + water

iv) Calcium hydroxide + **sulfuric acid** → calcium sulfate + water

Q2    Salts are prepared by the **neutralisation** of an **acid/alkali** and an **acid/alkali**. This also gives **water**. To make sure the acid and alkali are added in the right amounts an **indicator** is used to test the solution. **Universal indicator** is a good indicator to use. It goes **green** in a neutral solution. The type of acid used will give a particular salt. For example **sulfuric acid** will give a sulfate, hydrochloric acid will give a **chloride** and nitric acid will give a **nitrate**. All these are types of salts.

Q3  a) If a pure sample of salt is to be produced, then the right amounts of acid and alkali must be used. The right amounts will have been mixed when the alkali becomes neutralised by the added acid.

b) E.g. universal indicator

c) You do not want the salt crystals to be coloured by the indicator.

d) E.g. wear eye protection.

e) sodium chloride

Q4  a) potassium chloride

b) i) Water from the solution is evaporated, leaving behind a more concentrated salt solution.

ii) A solution in which no more salt can be dissolved.

c) i) smaller, bigger

ii) E.g. heat the salt solution using the Bunsen burner until all the water from the solution has evaporated. / Leave the salt solution in a warmer room.

## Pages 50-51 — Reactivity Series and Metal Extraction

Q1    potassium, magnesium, aluminium, zinc, iron, copper

Q2  a) lead — reduced by carbon
potassium — electrolysis
gold — very unreactive, found on its own
magnesium — electrolysis

b) E.g. lead can be extracted using carbon because it is less reactive than carbon. Gold is much less reactive than carbon — it is an unreactive metal and doesn't need to be extracted. Magnesium and potassium are more reactive than carbon, so they can't be extracted by reduction with carbon — electrolysis is used instead.

Q3    C

Q4  a) Rocks containing different metals and metal compounds (usually metal oxides).

b) carbon + iron oxide → iron + carbon dioxide

c) Aluminium is higher than carbon in the reactivity series / is more reactive than carbon.

d) electrolysis

## Pages 52-55 — Reactions of Metals with Acids

Q1

The mystery word is reaction.

Q2  a)

| Metal | Observations of reaction | Sound made by a lit splint above reaction |
|---|---|---|
| Zinc | Bubbled slightly | Squeaky pop |
| Magnesium | Bubbled vigorously | Big squeaky pop |
| Iron | Bubbled slightly | Squeaky pop |
| Copper | No reaction | No sound |

b) Hydrogen. The metal displaces the hydrogen from the acid.

Q3  a) i) 1.5 cm³

ii) 3.5 cm³

b) More violent, because calcium is higher than aluminium in the reactivity series.

Q4  a) They would react violently.

b) A big squeaky pop.

c) $2K + 2HCl \rightarrow 2KCl + H_2$

Q5

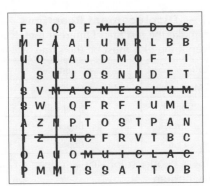

potassium, sodium, calcium, magnesium, aluminium, zinc, iron

Q6  a) potassium sulfate + hydrogen

b) sodium chloride + hydrogen

c) iron sulfate + hydrogen

d) No reaction — metal too unreactive.

e) magnesium sulfate + hydrogen

Q7    E.g. Can A. Can B is made from zinc — zinc is above hydrogen in the reactivity series, so zinc metal will react with the acidic orange juice to make hydrogen and zinc salts. The zinc salts will contaminate the orange segments and they won't be good to eat any more. Can A is made from copper. Copper is below hydrogen in the reactivity series so it doesn't react with the acidic orange juice.

# Answers

## Pages 56-57 — Reactions of Oxides with Acids

**Q1** a) iron + oxygen → **iron** oxide
b) **potassium** + oxygen → potassium oxide
c) **lead** + **oxygen** → lead oxide
d) carbon + oxygen → **carbon dioxide / carbon monoxide**
e) silicon + **oxygen** → **silicon** dioxide

**Q2** a) Metal oxides in solution have a pH **higher** than 7. This means that they are **alkaline**.
b) Non-metal oxides are **acidic** and have a pH **lower** than 7.
c) When a metal oxide reacts with an acid it produces **a salt** and **water**.

**Q3** a) Magnesium burns with a very bright white flame.
b) magnesium oxide

**Q4** a) alkali
b) lithium chloride
c) water

**Q5** a) phosphorus oxide
b) $P_4 + 5O_2 \rightarrow P_4O_{10}$
c) It would turn red/orange, showing that the solution is acidic.
d) The sodium hydroxide reacted with the acidic phosphorus oxide to make a salt and water, which are neutral.

**Q6** 1 — Non-metal
2 — Salt
3 — Alkali
4 — Sodium
5 — Metal
6 — Acid
7 — Lithium
The mystery element is silicon.

## Pages 58-61 — Displacement Reactions

**Q1** a) To make the test fair. Different metals are used so everything else must be the same.
b)

| Original metal | Deposited Metal |
|---|---|
| Magnesium | Copper |
| Copper | No deposit |
| Iron | Copper |
| Zinc | Copper |

c) zinc + copper sulphate → copper + zinc sulphate
d) magnesium
e) No change. Silver is less reactive than copper and will not displace it.

**Q2** a)

| Metal | Reaction with iron sulfate |
|---|---|
| Magnesium | ✔ |
| Aluminium | ✔ |
| Iron | ✗ |
| Lead | ✗ |
| Copper | ✗ |

b) iron
c) E.g. aluminium is more reactive than iron, so it will displace the iron from iron sulfate.

**Q3** a) magnesium
b) iron

c) lead
d) reactive
e) colourless
f) iron
The mystery metal is silver.

**Q4** a)

| Metal ↓ / Salt solution → | magnesium sulfate | aluminium sulfate | zinc sulfate | iron sulfate | copper sulfate |
|---|---|---|---|---|---|
| magnesium | | ✔ | ✔ | ✔ | ✔ |
| aluminium | | | ✔ | ✔ | ✔ |
| zinc | | | | ✔ | ✔ |
| iron | | | | | ✔ |
| copper | | | | | |

b) copper sulfate
c) It goes green.
d) zinc, aluminium, magnesium

**Q5** a) neutralisation
b) The **hydrogen** is **displaced** from hydrochloric acid by sodium by **sodium** from sodium hydroxide, forming a **salt** and water.
c) $NaOH + HCl \rightarrow NaCl + H_2O$

**Q6** a)

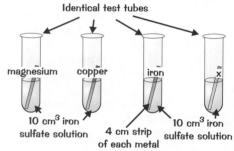

Identical test tubes

magnesium   copper   iron   x

10 cm³ iron sulfate solution   4 cm strip of each metal   10 cm³ iron sulfate solution

b) E.g. to see if either iron or metal X were more reactive than copper.
c) E.g. lead
d) The copper was displaced from its salt.
e) magnesium, iron, X, copper

## Section 3 — The Earth and The Atmosphere

### Pages 62-63 — The Earth's Structure

**Q1** a)

Mantle
Core
Crust

b) The Earth is almost a **sphere** and is made up of several layers. The **crust** is a thin layer of solid **rock**. The core is at the **centre** of the Earth.
c) i) The temperature increases as you go deeper into the mantle.
   ii) slowly
d) i) crust
   ii) core

**Q2** a) rocks ➡ minerals ➡ compounds ➡ elements
b) E.g. quartz

**Q3** a) Tectonic plates are large pieces of the Earth's crust and the upper mantle.
b) i) They 'float' on the mantle.
   ii) Slowly / A few centimetres per year.

# Answers

c) Tectonic plates moving very suddenly.

d) Volcanoes

## Pages 64-67 — Rock Types

**Q1** There are **three** different types of rock. Igneous rocks are made from melted underground rock called **magma**, which is pushed up towards the surface of the **crust** and sometimes out through **volcanoes**. Igneous rocks contain minerals arranged in interlocking **crystals**. The **size** of the crystals depends on how **fast** the rock cools down. **Large** crystals mean the rock cooled slowly. Sedimentary rocks are formed from **layers** of sediment laid down in lakes or **seas** over **millions** of years. The particles are then cemented together by other **minerals**. Sometimes the remains of long dead plants and animals are found in the rock. These are called **fossils**. Scientists study the fossil type to work out the **age** of the rock. Metamorphic rocks are formed by heating and increased pressure acting on existing rocks over **long** periods of time. Metamorphic rocks can contain tiny **crystals** and may also have **layers**.

**Q2** a) Extrusive and intrusive

b) Extrusive rocks are ejected by volcanoes and cool quickly above the ground. Intrusive rocks cool slowly underground and are eventually exposed when rocks above them wear away.

**Q3**

| Rock | Igneous | Sedimentary | Metamorphic |
|---|---|---|---|
| Basalt | ✓ | | |
| Chalk | | ✓ | |
| Slate | | | ✓ |
| Grit | | ✓ | |
| Granite | ✓ | | |
| Marble | | | ✓ |
| Breccia | | ✓ | |
| Obsidian | ✓ | | |
| Pumice | ✓ | | |
| Sandstone | | ✓ | |
| Marl | | ✓ | |
| Quartzite | | | ✓ |

**Q4** a) Layers of sediment are laid down over millions of years and cemented together by other minerals.

b) Rock 5, because the deeper in the Earth the sedimentary rock is, the longer ago it was formed.

c) It is formed from molten magma pushing up into the crust and cooling.

d) Rock 1 — rock 1 makes up the top layer of sedimentary rock. The age of sedimentary rock increases with depth, so the lower down the rock layer is, the older it is.

e) i) Syenite, because it has the largest average size crystals, meaning it cooled the slowest.

ii) Basalt, because it has the smallest average crystal size. Magma that erupts from volcanoes cools quickly above ground and produces rocks with small crystals.

**Q5** a) Rock fragments and dead matter

b) Borax is dissolved in the lake water. The water evaporates leaving solid borax behind.

## Pages 68-70 — The Rock Cycle

**Q1** a) transportation

b) exposure

c) deposition

d) weathering

e) burial/compression

f) melting

g) erosion

h) cooling

i) heating/pressure

**Q2** a) T

b) T

c) T

d) T

e) F

f) T

g) T

h) F

i) F

**Q3** a) Higher

b) Water collects in a crack in a rock. When the water freezes it expands, which can make the crack bigger. After freezing and thawing many times, bits break off.

**Q4** a) During the day, the Sun warms the surface of the rock. When the rock gets warm it expands. At night, the surface of the rock cools down and contracts.

b) The repeated cycles of expanding and contracting eventually cause bits to break off the rock.

c) Onion-skin weathering

**Q5**

| Label | Number |
|---|---|
| Sedimentary rocks | 7 |
| Metamorphic rocks | 8 |
| Sediments | 5 |
| Magma | 10 |
| Weathering | 2 |
| Erosion and transport | 3 |
| Extrusive igneous rock | 11 |
| Deposition | 4 |
| Exposure | 1 |
| Intrusive igneous rock | 12 |
| Melting | 9 |
| Burial, compression and cementation | 6 |

## Pages 71-72 — Recycling

**Q1** a) plastic bags, petrol, plastic cups

b) Millions of years ago, the remains of dead **plants** and animals were buried in the Earth's crust. Over time, the remains turned into fossil fuels like **crude oil**. Fossil fuels are **limited** resources because they take such a **long** time to make. Once all the fossil fuels have been used, we won't get any more for **millions of years**. We make a lot of things using fossil fuels — that's why **recycling** is important.

c) Taking old or unwanted products and using the materials to make new things.

# Answers

d)  1. It uses fewer limited resources.
    2. It uses less energy, which is expensive / usually comes from fossil fuels.
    3. It makes less rubbish, which ends up in landfill sites.

**Q2  a)** The aluminium has to be extracted.

**b)** It's usually cheaper to **recycle** materials rather than throwing them away and **making** new ones. It also costs money to send used aluminium to **landfill**. Recycling is generally much more **efficient** than making new materials all the time. For example, recycling aluminium cans uses 95% **less** energy than **mining** and extracting fresh aluminium. The **efficiency** varies depending on what is being recycled. Aluminium is **more** efficient to recycle than **plastic** or steel.

**c)** E.g. Recycling uses less energy than obtaining fresh aluminium — this energy usually comes from burning fossil fuels which is bad for the environment. Using freshly extracted aluminium will mean more aluminium ore has to be mined — mining uses lots of energy and makes a mess of the landscape. Using recycled aluminium also means less aluminium ends up in landfill sites.

## Pages 73-74 — The Carbon Cycle

**Q1  a)** photosynthesis

**b) i)** Green plants and algae should be circled.

**ii)** 1. carbohydrates  2. fats  3. proteins

**Q2  a)** carbon dioxide

**b)** E.g. they feed on dead plants, animals and animal waste. When the decomposers respire, carbon from the plants and animals is returned to the air in carbon dioxide.

**c) i)** Dead plant and animal remains that get buried and eventually form fossil fuels.

**ii)** By combustion / by burning them.

**Q3  a)**

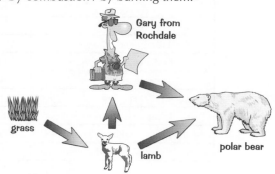

**b)** Fats and proteins.

**Q4**

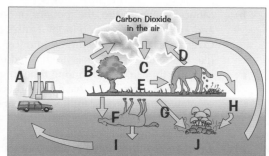

## Pages 75-76 — The Atmosphere and Climate

**Q1  a)** Gas A — Nitrogen
    Gas B — Oxygen

**b) i)** 0.04%

**ii)** E.g. water vapour

**Q2  a)** Cutting down trees.

**b)** E.g. it makes it increase because trees remove carbon dioxide from the atmosphere by photosynthesis. When there are fewer trees, less carbon dioxide is removed, so overall the level of carbon dioxide increases.

**Q3  a)** E.g. driving a car, making electricity.

**b) i)** E.g. energy from the Sun is trapped in the Earth's atmosphere by greenhouse gases. This stops the energy being lost into space and helps to keep the Earth warm.

**ii)** It's increasing.

**Q4  a)** Global warming is the name for the increase in the Earth's temperature.

**b)** The level of carbon dioxide/greenhouse gases in the Earth's atmosphere is increasing.

**c)** E.g.
Effect: Melting of the polar ice caps.
Explanation: Sea levels could rise and coastal areas could flood.
Effect: Rainfall patterns could change.
Explanation: It might be harder for farmers to grow crops.

# Physics
## Section 1 — Energy and Matter
### Page 1 — Energy Transfer

**Q1  a)** chemical

**b)** magnetic

**c)** electrostatic

**d)** kinetic

**Q2** Energy in the chemical energy stores of the food we eat is transferred into different energy stores. For example, it is transferred to our kinetic energy stores when we move or to our body's thermal energy stores to keep it warm.

**Q3  b)** Thermal energy store is increasing.
Chemical energy store is decreasing.

**c)** Kinetic energy store is increasing.
Elastic potential energy store is decreasing.

**d)** E.g. Gravitational potential energy store of the box is increasing.
Chemical energy store of the postman is decreasing.

**e)** Kinetic energy store is increasing.
Gravitational potential energy store is decreasing.

### Page 2 — More Energy Transfer

**Q1** Energy transferred = force × distance

**Q2  a)** When the battery and heater are connected in a **complete** electrical circuit, energy is transferred from the **chemical** energy store of the battery to the **thermal** energy store of the heater. The energy is transferred **electrically**.

**b)** by heating

# Answers

**Q3** **a)** Energy transferred = force × distance
= 200 × 15
= **3000 J**
**b)** gravitational potential (energy)
**Q4** smaller

## Pages 3-4 — Energy Transfer By Heating
**Q1** **a)** False
**b)** True
**c)** True
**d)** False
**e)** False
**f)** False
**Q2** When **energy** is transferred between objects of different temperatures, it tends to **reduce** the temperature difference. Energy is transferred from the **thermal** energy store of the **hotter** to the same energy store of the **cooler** object. When the two objects reach **thermal** equilibrium it means they are at the same **temperature**.
**Q3** **a)** radiation
**b)** conduction
**c)** radiation
**d)** conduction
**Q4** **a)** Metals are conductors so they transfer energy quickly to the food / it will heat up and cook the food quickly.
**b)** Metal is a conductor, so it will quickly transfer energy to your hand and burn you. Plastic is an insulator, so it will transfer energy to your hand much slower, so you won't get a burn.
**Q5** **a)** The hot drink
**b)** The cold drink
**c)** The cold drink

## Page 5 — Conservation of Energy
**Q1** The principle of conservation of energy states that energy can never be **created** nor **destroyed**, but is only **transferred** from one energy store to another.
**Q2** **a)** no
**b)** by heating
**c)** wasted energy
**Q3**

| | Useful Energy Output Store | Wasted Energy Transferred By |
|---|---|---|
| **a)** | kinetic | sound |
| **b)** | kinetic | heating |
| **c)** | thermal | sound |

**Q4** **a)** Total energy input
= Useful energy + Wasted energy
= 2500 + 500 = **3000 J**
**b)**

```
                        mechanically  ┌────────────────────────┐
                      ───────────────▶│ gravitational potential │
┌───────────────────┐                 │ energy store of the    │
│ kinetic energy    │                 │ object                 │
│ store of the motor│                 │ 2500 J                 │
│ 3000 J            │                 └────────────────────────┘
│                   │  by heating     ┌────────────────────────┐
└───────────────────┘ ───────────────▶│ thermal energy store   │
                                      │ of the surroundings    │
                                      │ 500 J                  │
                                      └────────────────────────┘
```

## Page 6 — Energy Resources
**Q1** The Sun transfers a great deal of energy to the Earth by **light** and by heating. Plants can trap this energy and change it by a process called **photosynthesis**. Creatures can absorb this energy by eating the plants. When plants and animals **die** they can become buried and over millions of years they are turned into coal, **oil/gas** and **gas/oil**. We call fuels formed in this way **fossil** fuels.
**Q2** **a)** the Sun
**b)** wind and waves
**c)** E.g. wood/food
**d)** It is transferred into the kinetic energy store of the wind and then transferred into the kinetic energy store of the waves.

## Page 7 — Generating Electricity
**Q1** **a)** chemical
**b)** thermal
**c)** kinetic to electrostatic
**Q2** **a)** One day they will run out.
**b)** Fossil fuels are made over millions of years, and only take a few minutes to burn. Once we've used them all, there will be no more.
**c)** E.g. gas for cooking/coal for fires.
**d)** Any two of: e.g. save energy (turning off lights) / use more renewable energy resources / recycle more
**Q3** **a)** They depend on the Sun, so as long as the Sun shines, they won't run out.
**b)** renewable

## Pages 8-9 — The Cost of Electricity
**Q1** **a) i)** An appliance that needs electricity to work/uses electricity as its 'fuel'.
**ii)** How fast an electrical appliance transfers energy.
**iii)** Inkjet-DJ
**b)** Energy transferred (kWh)
= Power (kW) × Time (h)
= 0.4 × 2 = **0.8 kWh**
**c)** Cost = Energy transferred (kWh) × Price per kWh
= 0.8 × 15p = **12p**
**Q2** 1.5 minutes = 90 seconds
Energy transferred (J)
= Power (W) × Time (s)
= 700 × 90 = **63 000 J**
**Q3** **a) i)** kilowatt-hours
**ii)** E.g. a gas meter
**b) i)** Energy transferred (kWh)
= Power (kW) × Time (h)
= 0.1 × 1.5 = **0.15 kWh**
**ii)** Rob has assumed that the spotlights were the only thing in his house using electricity, when in reality he will have had other things turned on too.
**iii)** Energy transferred
= 9927.97 − 9927.37 = 0.6 kWh
Cost = Energy transferred (kWh) × Price per kWh
= 0.6 kWh × 12p = **7.2p**

## Page 10 — Comparing Power Ratings and Energy Values
**Q1** The power rating of an appliance is how much **energy** it transfers per second when it is operating at its recommended **maximum** power. The **higher** the power rating, the **higher** the amount of energy transferred in a given time.

# Answers

Appliances with **higher** power ratings will cost more to run over a given time than appliances with **lower** power ratings.

**Q2 a)** kilojoules

**b)** It is important to make sure you're taking in the right amount of energy each day.

**c)** Choco Cookie Crunch Cereal

**Q3 a)** Power drill A

**b)** Power drill A has the lowest power, so it transfers the least amount of electrical energy over a set period of time, so it will have the lowest electricity costs.

## Pages 11-12 — Physical Changes

**Q1 a)** dissolving

**b)** melting

**c)** freezing

**d)** condensing

**e)** melting, evaporating (in any order)

**Q2** The arrangement of the water particles changes, the water becomes less dense.

**Q3 a)** It doesn't.

**b)** The number of salt particles stays the same, they are just in a different arrangement.

**c)** It doesn't.

**d)** 5 g

**Q4 a)** sublimation

**b)** It stays the same.

**c)** A solid turning into a gas is an example of a **physical** change.

**d)** There's no actual reaction taking place and no new substances are made, the particles just rearrange their positions and have different energies.

**Q5 a)** The particles become more closely packed together.

**b)** The density will increase.

**c)** Heating a liquid causes the particles to move around more, and move further apart, causing it to turn into a gas.

## Pages 13-14 — Movement of Particles

**Q1 a)** randomly / with zigzag motion

**b)** Brownian motion

**Q2 a)**

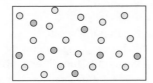

**b)** All the gas particles move around with random zigzag / Brownian motion. The gas B particles eventually bump and jiggle their way from an area of high concentration to an area of low concentration. They will constantly bump into each other until they're evenly spread out amongst the gas A particles.

**Q3 a)** As the temperature increases, the mercury particles get more energy and move around more — their speed increases. This means the space between particles gets bigger, so the mercury takes up more space.

**b)** As the temperature decreases, the pressure of the liquid mercury on the glass tube **decreases**. This is because the particles get **slower** and bump into the sides of the glass tube **less**.

**Q4** Smoke particles are **big** and heavy. When observed in a lab, they appear to move randomly. This is because of the **Brownian** motion caused by **small** air particles. They travel at **high** speeds, bumping into the **smoke** particles and **moving** them around.

## Section 2 — Forces and Motion
### Pages 15-16 — Speed

**Q1 a)** Speed is a measure of how far you travel in a set amount of time.

**b)** Average speed is worked out from dividing **distance** by **time**.

**c)** miles per hour, metres per second, kilometres per hour

**Q2** speed = distance ÷ time — s = d ÷ t
time = distance ÷ speed — t = d ÷ s
distance = speed × time — d = s × t

**Q3**

| Distance (m) | Time (s) | Speed (m/s) |
|---|---|---|
| 10 | 5 | 2 |
| 0.5 | 2 | 0.25 |
| 1000 | 10 | 100 |
| 20 | 0.1 | 200 |
| 500 | 50 | 10 |
| 48 | 4 | 12 |
| 1 | 0.01 | 100 |
| 10 | 50 | 0.2 |
| 225 | 15 | 15 |

**Q4** Speed = Distance ÷ Time
= 7000 miles ÷ 14 hours = **500 mph**

**Q5 a)** 3 minutes = 3 ÷ 60 = 0.05 hours

**b)** Speed = Distance ÷ Time, so
Distance = Speed × Time
= 40 km/h × 0.05 hours = **2 km**

**Q6**

| Distance | Time | Speed |
|---|---|---|
| 140 miles | 2 h | 70 mph |
| 50 km | 5 hours | 10 km/h |
| 2 m | 100 years | 2 cm per year |
| 150 000 000 km | 500 s | 300 000 km/s |
| 1 km | 200 s | 5 m/s |
| 1 km | 20 s | 50 m/s |
| 600 m | 1 minute | 10 m/s |
| 72 km | 2 h | 10 m/s |
| 360 km | 3600 s | 100 m/s |
| 360 km | 60 minutes | 100 m/s |
| 45 miles | 45 minutes | 60 mph |
| 55 km | 30 minutes | 110 km/h |

# Answers

## Pages 17-18 — More on Speed

**Q1 a)** The object is stationary.
**b) i)** The object's speed is constant.
 **ii)** The speed of the object.
**c)** 4-8s: The cat is stationary.
 8-10s: The cat is moving at (a steady speed of) 1 m/s.
 10-12s: The cat is moving at (a steady speed of) 2 m/s in the other direction.
**d) i)** Its speed is increasing.
 **ii)** acceleration
 **iii)** The object's speed is decreasing.

**Q2 a)** Two trains are moving towards each other along a straight line. To find the speed of one train relative to the other train, you need to **add** their speeds.
**b)** Two trains are moving in the same direction along a straight line. To find the speed of one train relative to the other train, you need to **subtract** their speeds.

**Q3 a)** Relative speed = Brad's speed + Lee's speed = 24 mph + 33 mph = **57 mph**
**b)** Brad is moving towards Lee, so Lee is getting closer much faster than he would if Brad were still.

**Q4 a)** Relative speed = speed of taxi – speed of car = 18 m/s – 12 m/s = **6 m/s**
**b)** Relative speed = speed of taxi – speed of car = 18 m/s – 0 m/s = **18 m/s**

## Pages 19-20 — Forces and Movement

**Q1** Forces are measured in **newtons** and can be measured using a **newton meter**. They are either **pushes/pulls** or **pulls/pushes** that occur when two **objects** interact. They usually act in **pairs**.

**Q2 a)** True
**b)** False
**c)** False
**d)** True

**Q3** Speed up or start moving — hitting a snooker ball
Change direction — a tennis ball bouncing off a wall
Change shape — stretching an elastic band
Turn — unscrewing a bottle lid
Slow down or stop moving — applying the brakes on a bicycle

**Q4 a)** balanced
**b)** unbalanced
**c)** unbalanced
**d)** balanced
**e)** unbalanced

**Q5** Shark — unbalanced
Helicopter — balanced
Car — unbalanced

**Q6 a)** speeds up
**b)** slows down
**c)** speeds up
**d)** stationary
**e)** steady speed
**f)** slows down

## Pages 21-23 — Friction and Resistance

**Q1 a)** Friction is a type of **force**.
**b)** Friction is measured in **newtons**.
**c)** Friction always acts to make moving objects travel more **slowly**.
**d)** The direction that friction acts is always **opposite to** the direction of motion.
**e)** Air and water both exert **decelerating** forces upon objects moving through them.
**f)** When an object moves through air the force of friction is called **drag**.
**g)** Friction forces in air or water increase as an object travels more **quickly** through it.

**Q2** When the force of friction equals the accelerating force the object will **continue at the same speed**.

**Q3** The chains give more friction between the wheels and the road, stopping the car from sliding on the ice.

**Q4**

| Situation | Friction should be... |
|---|---|
| A car tyre in contact with a road surface | high |
| A skater moving over the ice | low |
| Brake blocks pressing against a wheel rim | high |
| Rock climbing boots in contact with the rock | high |
| Pushing a box along the ground | low |

**Q5 a)** Driving force
**b)** It will increase.
**c)** The frictional force has increased.
**d)** Balanced
**e)** The speed is constant.
**f)** The forces must become unbalanced.
**g)** Friction/air resistance
**h)** It could be made more streamlined.
**i)** Weight and the reaction from the ground.

**Q6 a)** Weight
**b)** Drag/air resistance
**c)** No
**d)** Drag/air resistance increases with increasing speed.
**e)** Constant
**f)** B (drag/air resistance)
**g)** It will decrease.

**Q7 a)** They must all be the same weight.
**b)** B. It is more streamlined than the others.

## Page 24 — Force Diagrams

**Q1 a)** Downwards
**b)** Reaction
**c)** Upwards (in the opposite direction to the weight)
**d)** 35 N
**e)**

Reaction 35 N

Weight 35 N

# Answers

**Q2**
Boat:
Overall force = 500 N – 700 N = **–200 N**
The boat is **decelerating**.
Car:
Overall force = 6 500 N – 900 N = **5 600 N**
The car is **accelerating**.
Skydiver:
Overall force = 850 N – 850 N = **0 N**
The skydiver is **moving at a constant speed**.

**Q3**

Engine Force                    Drag /
                                air resistance

22 000 N                        2 000 N

## Pages 25-27 — Moments

**Q1**

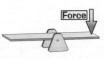

It will accelerate downwards

It will rotate clockwise

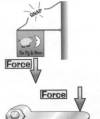

It will accelerate to the right

It will rotate anti-clockwise

It will rotate clockwise

It will accelerate downwards

**Q2** **a)** A moment is a measure of the **turning** effect of a force.

**b)** When a force acts on something with a **pivot**, it can create a moment.

**c)** Moments are measured in **Nm**.

**d)** The moment is increased if the size of the force is **increased.**

**e)** The moment is also increased if the force acts at a **greater** perpendicular distance from the **pivot**.

**Q3** **a)** Moment caused by Anna's weight
= Force × Perpendicular distance
= **300** N × **2** m
= **600 Nm**
Moment caused by Aaron's weight
= Force × Perpendicular distance
= **400** N × **2** m
= **800 Nm**

**b)** Clockwise. Aaron's clockwise moment is greater than Anna's anticlockwise moment.

**c)** Moving closer to the pivot decreases the moment caused by his weight. He has moved until the moment of his weight balances the moment of Anna's weight. It would be easier at the edge.

**Q4** Moment = force × distance from pivot, so if the DJ exerts the same force at both points, the further his fingers are from the middle of the record, the greater the moment.

**Q5** **a)** clockwise
**b)** 30 cm
**c)** Moment = Force × Distance
= 200 N × 0.3 m = **60 Nm**
**d)** 60 Nm
**e)** The distance of force B from the pivot has increased, so the moment created by force B has increased. To balance this moment, the moment created by force A must increase, and so force A should be moved further from the pivot.

**Q6** Ruler A is **balanced**, and it will **not move**.
Ruler B is **unbalanced**, and it will **rotate clockwise**.

## Pages 28-30 — Forces and Elasticity

**Q1** **a) i)** Changing the shape of an object.
**ii)** An object that returns back to its original shape after being deformed/stretched or compressed.
**b)** E.g. a spring
**c)** E.g. a drinks can. It does not return to its original shape when compressed/squashed.

**Q2** Dennis **deforms** the elastic by **stretching** it. He is doing **work** by transferring energy from the elastic's **kinetic** energy store to its **elastic potential** energy store.
When he releases the elastic, it returns to its original **shape** and energy is transferred back to its **kinetic** energy store.

**Q3** **a) i)** F is the **force**.
It is measured in **newtons (N)**.
**ii)** k is the **spring constant**.
It is measured in **newtons per metre (N/m)**.
**iii)** e is the **extension**.
It is measured in **metres (m)**.
**b)** The extension of a spring is directly proportional to the force applied to the spring.
**c) i)** Hookes Law works for **some materials**.
**ii)** Hooke's Law only applies **up to** a certain force.
**iii)** The force at which Hooke's Law stops working for springs is **higher** than for most other materials.
**d)** Force = spring constant × extension
= 60 N/m × 0.1 m = **6 N**

**Q4** **a)** 10 N
**b)** Upwards (in the opposite direction to the weight).
**c)** The forces on the spring are in **equilibrium**.

**Q5** **a)**

| Weight (N) | 0 | 2 | 4 | 6 | 8 | 10 |
|---|---|---|---|---|---|---|
| Length of spring (cm) | 20 | 24 | 28 | 32 | 38 | 55 |
| Extension of spring (cm) | 0 | **4** | **8** | **12** | **18** | **35** |

**b)**

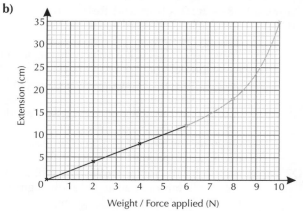

Weight / Force applied (N)

**c)** The graph is a straight line at first, so the extension is directly proportional to the force applied.

**d)** The graph stops being a straight line so the extension is no longer directly proportional to the force applied.

## Pages 31-34 — Pressure

**Q1 a)** Pressure measures the **force** applied to a certain **area**.

**b)** Pressure is calculated using the force applied at **90°** to an area.

**c)** The more force there is over a given area, the **greater** the pressure.

**d)** The greater the area over which the force acts, the **smaller** the pressure.

**e)** Pressure is worked out from dividing **force** by **area**.

**f)** Force is measured in **newtons**.

**g)** Area is measured in **m²**.

**h)** Pressure is measured in either **pascals** or **N/m²**.

**Q2 a) i)** She has not taken into account the shape of her shoes.

**ii)** too big

**b)** For both her feet.

**c)** Area = 2 × 0.2 × 0.05 = 0.02 m²
Pressure = Force ÷ Area
= 500 N ÷ 0.02 = **25 000 Pa**

**d)** She could measure the area of her shoes more accurately.

**Q3** Pressure = Force ÷ Area
A = F ÷ p
Force = Pressure × Area

**Q4 a)** If a force of 1 **N** is spread over an **area** of 1 m², then it exerts a **pressure** of 1 **Pa** .

**b)** 75 pascals (Pa)

**Q5 a) i)** 2400 N
**ii)** 2 m × 3 m = **6 m²**
**iii)** Pressure = Force ÷ Area
= 2400 N ÷ 6 m² = **400 Pa** or **400 N/m²**

**b)** Force = Pressure × Area
= 9000 N/m² × 6 m² = **54 000 N**

**c)** The pressure will be greater because the same force is now acting over a smaller area.

**Q6 a)** For a given force, blunt scissors have a greater area so they give a lower pressure.

**b)** In case 1, there is a high pressure on the board because the area at the tip of the pin is small, so the pin is pushed into the board. In case 2 the area in contact with the board is large, so the pressure is small, and the pin is not pushed in.

**c)** Caterpillar tracks have a large surface area compared to wheels, so the weight of the vehicle is spread over a larger area. This means a lower pressure and so the vehicle is less likely to sink.

**Q7**

| Object | Area should be: (large / small) | Pressure will be: (high / low) |
|---|---|---|
| A knife edge | Small | High |
| Shoe heels that don't damage floors | Large | Low |
| A sewing needle | Small | High |
| Tractor tyres for use on soft ground | Large | Low |
| Snow skis | Large | Low |

**Q8** As the balloon gets higher there is **less** atmosphere above it so the weight of the atmosphere pressing down on it **decreases**. The area of the balloon that this weight is acting on **stays the same**, and so the atmospheric pressure on the balloon **decreases**. When the balloon loses height there is **more** atmosphere above it. The weight of the atmosphere pressing down on it **increases** and so the atmospheric pressure on the balloon **increases**.

**Q9** The submarine experiences water pressure from all directions. Water pressure increases with depth, so the force pushing upwards on the bottom of the submarine is larger than the force pushing downwards on the top of the submarine. So the pressure causes an overall upwards force (upthrust).

**Q10** Duck — float
Book — sink
Apple — float

## Section 3 — Waves
### Pages 35-36 — Water Waves

**Q1 a)** The undulations of the water wave are **at right-angles to** the direction the wave is travelling in.

**b) i)** energy
**ii)** It is transferred in the direction that the wave is travelling in.

**c)** The wave will be reflected / it will change direction.

**Q2 a)**

**b)** How far a point on the wave is from the middle line.

**c)** E.g. a water wave / light.

**Q3 a)** When two (or more) waves meet and their displacements combine.

# Answers

b) i) A trough that is twice the depth of the individual wave troughs.
ii) A crest that is double the height of the individual wave crests.
c) E.g.

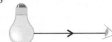

Accept any correct wave diagram with an amplitude of 1 cm at its crest.
d) The waves that meet in the middle of the tank must have troughs and crests with the same amplitude. When they meet they cancel each other out.

## Pages 37-38 — Light Waves
Q1 a) An object that produces light.
b) Any three of, e.g. the Sun, light bulbs, candles, glow worms.
Q2 a) E.g.

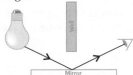

Accept any straight line drawn from the bulb to the pupil of the eye with an arrow pointing in the correct direction.
b) E.g.

Accept any answer that shows a light ray travelling in a straight line from the bulb, being reflected off the mirror's surface and travelling in a straight line into the pupil of the eye.
Q3 a) Both
b) Both
c) Both
d) Light only
e) Both
Q4 a) A vacuum is anywhere where there are no **particles** at all.
b) $3 \times 10^8$ m/s
c) nothing
Q5 a) Light waves don't need particles to travel, but water waves do — they travel by moving particles. There aren't any particles in a vacuum so water waves can't travel though them, but light waves can.
b) Light waves travel faster through a vacuum than in air because light waves are slowed down by particles.

## Pages 39-43 — Reflection and Refraction
Q1 a) Some light is reflected and some light travels through the surface.
b) Transparent objects are objects that light will travel through, but light can't travel through opaque objects. Shiny objects are smooth and reflect a lot of light.
c) Transparent: any three of, e.g. glasses, windows, jam jars, glasses lenses, milk bottles.
Opaque: any three of, e.g. trees, bricks, concrete, doors, walls, people.
Q2 a) Mirrors have a very **smooth** shiny surface. When light hits a mirror at an angle, all the light is **reflected** at the **same** angle, giving a clear reflection. This is known as **specular** reflection.
b) Rough surfaces like paper look dull because the light that hits them is reflected back in lots of different directions — the light is scattered.
Q3 a) Angle of incidence = angle of reflection.
b) Mirror

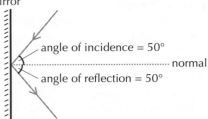

(You could also have drawn the light ray travelling the same path but in the opposite direction. In that case the angle of incidence and angle of reflection would be drawn the other way round.)
Q4 a) Any substance that light or any other wave travels through is called a medium.
b) When light is travelling through a medium it **travels in a straight line**. When light moves from one medium into another, its speed **is** changed. If the light enters the new medium at an angle to the boundary, it continues to travel in a **straight** line in the new medium, but with a new direction. This change happens because the speed of light is **different** in different materials. The name given to this effect is **refraction**.
Q5 a) D
b) Because the light ray enters the glass block travelling straight on / along the normal.
Q6 a) i) and ii)
E.g.

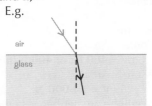

Accept any answer which shows the ray bent towards the normal.

**b)** The light changes direction because the light travels from a material with a lower density to a material with a higher density. This causes the speed of the light ray to decrease as it crosses the boundary between the air and glass and it bends towards the normal.

**Q7** He has shown the light ray from the fish bending towards the normal at the water's surface. The ray should bend away from the normal because water is denser than air.

**Q8**

**Q9**

| | | | | | | | | | | | |
|---|---|---|---|---|---|---|---|---|---|---|---|
| T | R | A | N | S | P | A | R | E | N | T | Light will travel through ____ materials |
| | R | E | F | R | A | C | T | | | | When it moves from one material to another light can ____ |
| D | I | F | F | U | S | E | | | | | Rough surfaces look dull because of ____ scattering |
| | R | A | Y | | | | | | | | A light wave is also known as a light ____ |
| | A | N | G | L | E | | | | | | ____ of incidence = ____ of reflection |
| S | P | E | C | U | L | A | R | | | | ____ reflection — a clear reflection from a surface, e.g. a mirror |
| | T | O | W | A | R | D | S | | | | Going from air to glass, light bends ____ the normal |
| D | E | N | S | I | T | Y | | | | | Light travels slower in a material with greater ____ |
| | O | P | A | Q | U | E | | | | | Light can't travel through ____ materials |
| N | O | R | M | A | L | | | | | | The line at right-angles to a surface |

## Pages 44-46 — How We See

**Q1 a)** The object being viewed — B
Tracing paper — A
Pinhole — C

**b)** Light travels in **straight** lines from the object being viewed through the **pinhole** towards the **tracing paper**. The pinhole is very **small**, so only one **ray** from each point on the object gets into the camera.

**c)**

**d)** E.g.

The image of the eagle is upside down and crossed over because the rays of light cross over as they pass through the pinhole.

**Q2** 1 — Light is produced by the Sun.
2 — Light is reflected by non-luminous objects.
3 — Some of the reflected light travels towards our eyes.
4 — The cornea of each eye focuses most of the incoming light.
5 — The lens changes shape to focus the light depending on the distance of the object.
6 — An image is formed on the retina.

**Q3 a) i)** iris
**ii)** retina
**iii)** lens
**iv)** cornea

**b)**

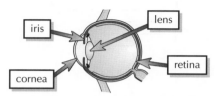

**Q4** An image formed on the eye's retina will be **upside down**.

**Q5 a)** refraction

**b)** E.g.

Light → Focus

**Convex lens**

**Q6 a)** Anything that absorbs energy transferred by light.

**b)** E.g. a retina cell in the eye / a film in a film camera / a digital sensor in a digital camera.

**c)** energy

**Q7 a)** E.g. Energy is transferred to his retina by the light, causing electrical and chemical changes in special cells. The special cells then send signals to his brain.

**b)** E.g. Energy is transferred to the sensor by the light, causing it to generate an electrical charge. Changes in charge are read by a computer and turned into an image.

## Pages 47-50 — Colour

**Q1 a)** Light from the Sun and light bulbs is often called **white** light.

**b)** Light can be split into its colours using a **prism**.

**c)** This splitting is called **dispersal**.

**d)** The pattern of colours made like this is called a **spectrum**.

**e)** In order, the seven main colours are red, **orange**, **yellow**, **green**, **blue**, **indigo** and **violet**.

**f)** Different colours are caused by light waves having different **frequencies**.

**g)** Red light has a **lower** frequency than violet light.

**h)** The number of **waves** of light that pass a point per second is called the frequency.

**Q2 a)** A post box is red because the paint on it diffusely **reflects** red light and **absorbs** all the other colours. A dandelion flower appears yellow because it absorbs **all** the colours of light except for **yellow**.

# Answers

b) i)   All colours.
   ii)  No colours
c)      No colours.

**Q3 a)** Light that is the same colour as the filter.
**b)** The torch now shines with a red light. All of the colours of white light from the torch are absorbed except for red.
**c)**

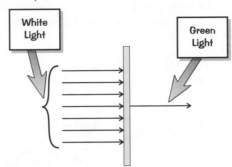

d) i)   red
   ii)  It isn't red.

**Q4 a)**

| Colour of cube | Colour of light | Colour cube seems to be |
|---|---|---|
| White | Red | Red |
|  | Blue | Blue |
|  | Green | Green |
| Red | Red | **Red** |
|  | Green | **Black** |
|  | **Blue** | Black |
| Blue | **Red** | Black |
|  | **Blue** | Blue |
|  | Green | **Black** |
| Green | Red | Black |
|  | Blue | Black |
|  | Green | Green |
| Black | Green | **Black** |
|  | Blue | **Black** |
|  | Red | **Black** |

**b)** Yes. A coloured filter only lets through light of the colour that it is. So for example, using a red filter will only let through the red light, so it is the same as if you only shone red light in the first place.

**Q5 a)** A blue car would appear black because there is no blue light for it to reflect, and it absorbs the orange light.
An orange car would appear orange because it reflects the orange light.
A white car would appear orange because white objects reflect all colours of light, so the orange light would be reflected.
**b)** A blue car would appear blue.
An orange car would appear orange.
A white car would appear white.
**c)** Because everything appears its actual colour in white light.

**Q6** black

## Pages 51-52 — Sound

**Q1 a) i)** ✔
   **ii)** ✘
   **iii)** ✔
**b)** The vibrations in longitudinal waves are parallel to the direction of the wave.
**Q2** Sounds travel through **mediums**. When something vibrates, it passes on the sound **vibrations** to the particles next to it. These vibrations are then passed through the medium as a series of **compressions** — regions of squashed-up particles.
**Q3 a)** E.g. when the air was removed, there was a vacuum inside the jar. Sound can't travel in a vacuum as there are no particles to pass on the vibrations.
**b) i)** It's soft.
   **ii)** E.g. curtains, carpets.
**Q4 a)** A higher frequency means **more** vibrations per second.
**b)** Frequency is a measure of **pitch**.
**c)** A **high** frequency means a high-pitched sound.
**d)** Frequency is measured in **hertz** — which is the number of vibrations per second.
**Q5 a)** E.g. light travels much faster than sound, so the light waves reached his eyes before the sound waves reached his ears.
**b)** E.g. the explosion caused sound waves in the ground and in the air. Because the ground is a solid, it has more particles than air, which is a gas. So the ground is denser than the air. The more particles there are in a medium / the denser a medium is, the faster a sound wave travels. So the sound waves travelled faster through the ground and reached Russell sooner.
**c)** E.g. the sound waves were reflected off the south side of the quarry and back towards Russell.

## Pages 53-54 — Hearing

**Q1** A — ear flap
B — ear drum
C — ear bones
D — auditory nerve
E — cochlea
**Q2** 2 — The vibrations of the tuning fork are passed to the air particles.
4 — The ear drum vibrates.
7 — A message is sent to the brain along the auditory nerve.
5 — The ear bones vibrate.
3 — The air particles vibrate.
1 — The tuning fork vibrates.
6 — Hairs in the cochlea vibrate.
**Q3 a)** auditory range
**b) i)** 40 000 Hz
   **ii)** bottlenose dolphin
   **iii)** bottlenose dolphin
**c)** The bottom string on a guitar, a person talking.

# Answers

## Pages 55-57 — Energy and Waves

**Q1** When **waves** transfer energy from one place to another, they can also transfer **information**. Sound waves do this through **vibrations** between **particles**, where the pressure changes. This is useful for **recording** and replaying sounds.

**Q2** **a)** 1 — thin paper
2 — thin plastic sheet
**b)** E.g. as sound waves / by vibrating the particles in the air.
**c)** E.g. the vibrations in a sound wave make the diaphragm vibrate inside the microphone. The microphone turns the vibrations into electrical signals.
**d)** E.g. a loudspeaker.

**Q3** H ⟹ G ⟹ A

**Q4** When the diaphragm vibrates quickly, the speaker will make a high-pitched sound.

**Q5** **a)** Ultrasound waves have a higher pitch/frequency than the normal auditory range of humans.
**b)** greater than 20 000 Hz

**Q6** **a)** Water or another liquid.
**b)** The **energy** in high-pressure ultrasound waves causes **bubbles** to form in cavities. The bubbles knock **contaminants** off the object, leaving it **clean**.

**Q7** **a)** E.g. ultrasound pressure waves can transfer energy through matter, so they can reach inside the body to where the pain is.
**b) i)** Make sure both people have pain in the same muscle, make sure the people are about the same age.
**ii)** Ultrasound physiotherapy doesn't have any effect on muscle pain.
**iii)** E.g. test more people / use a bigger sample / repeat the experiment.

## Section 4 — Electricity and Magnetism
### Pages 58-59 — Electrical Circuits

**Q1** **a)** true
**b)** false
**c)** true
**d)** true
**e)** false

**Q2** Pump — Power supply
Pipes — Wires
Water flow — Electric current
Radiator — Heater

**Q3** **a)** Conventional current flows around the circuit from positive to negative. The electrons always flow in the opposite direction to the conventional current.
**b)** The current in a circuit **does not get** used up as it flows round the circuit.

**Q4** **a)** potential difference
**b)** E.g. batteries can have different potential differences.
**c)** E.g. more current will flow because the potential difference has increased.

**Q5** **a)** Anything in a circuit that slows down the flow of current.

**b) i)**

| Material | Bulb brightness | Resistance in Ω |
|----------|-----------------|-----------------|
| A | brightly lit | 0.01 |
| B | unlit | 100 |
| C | dimly lit | 10 |

**ii)** Material A
**c) i)** resistance = potential difference ÷ current
**ii)** Material B

## Pages 60-61 — Measuring Current and Potential Difference

**Q1** **a)** amperes / amps
**b)** ammeter
**c)** 2 A

**Q2** **a)** voltmeter
**b)** volts
**c)**

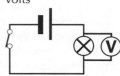

**Q3** **a)** The potential difference it will supply.
**b)** No, 5 V is the maximum potential difference that can be safely put across the bulb. The battery supplies 12 V which is higher than 5 V.

**Q4**
Switch (open) ⊸⌒o⊸
Buzzer ⟋⟍
Bulb ⊗
Ammeter Ⓐ
Battery ⊣|||⊢
Cell ⊣⊢
Motor Ⓜ

**Q5** E.g.

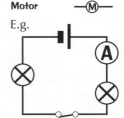

## Pages 62-64 — Series and Parallel Circuits

**Q1** **a)** Series because e.g. the current has no choice of route.
**b) i)** 2 A, because current is the same everywhere in the circuit.
**ii)** 0 A, because the open switch stops current flowing in the entire circuit.
**c)** 2 A

**Q2** A — same
B — dimmer
C — brighter

**Q3**

| Change to original circuit | Bulb(s) on | Bulb(s) off |
|----------------------------|------------|-------------|
| Bulb A is unscrewed | B, D, E | A, C |
| Bulb D is unscrewed | A, C, E | B, D |
| Bulb E is unscrewed | | A, B, C, D, E |

# Answers

**Q4** a) No
 b) Yes
 c) Yes
 d) Yes
 e) Bigger. The potential difference of the cell is shared between all the components in a series circuit. There are now less components in the circuit so the potential difference across bulb 1 must be bigger.

**Q5** a) F
 b) F
 c) T
 d) T
 e) F

**Q6** a) Ammeter $A_3$: 9 A
   Ammeter $A_4$: 10 A
 b) The current flows out of the cell, and it all flows through ammeter $A_1$. Then it splits into two routes. Some of the current flows through ammeter $A_2$ and bulb 1. Some of the current flows through the switch, ammeter $A_3$ and bulb 2. Then the two currents join up again and flow through ammeter $A_4$ and back to the cell.
 c) If one bulb blows, the other bulb will stay lit. If they were wired in series, then if one bulb were to blow they would both go out.
 d) Both will be 1.5 V.

## Pages 65-66 — Static Electricity

**Q1** a) Atoms contain positive and negative **charges**.
 b) Electrons are the **negative** parts of atoms.
 c) **Electrons** can move, but **positive charges** can't.
 d) Electrons can be **transferred** when two insulating objects are rubbed together.
 e) When an object gains electrons, it becomes **negatively** charged.
 f) An object that **loses** electrons is left with a positive charge.

**Q2** a) E.g. electrons from the cloth are scraped off and left on the rod. Because the rod has gained electrons it becomes negatively charged.
 b) The cloth has lost electrons (they were scraped off onto the rod), so the cloth has a positive charge overall.
 c) i) False
   ii) True
   iii) True
   iv) False

**Q3** a)

| Charge of object 1 | Charge of object 2 | Force between objects |
|---|---|---|
| Positive | Positive | Repulsion |
| Positive | Negative | Attraction |
| Negative | Positive | Attraction |
| Negative | Negative | Repulsion |

 b) It's the same as the second row.
 c) Opposite charges **attract**, charges of the same type **repel**.

**Q4** a) The space around a charged object where other charged objects will feel a force.
 b) Yes, electrons were transferred to the balloon. You know this because the balloon gained a negative charge.
 c) Each hair has a positive charge, so they repel each other.

## Pages 67-68 — Magnets

**Q1** a) bar magnet
 b) magnetic field lines
 c)

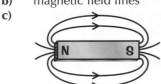

**Q2** a) E.g. he would see the iron filings line up with the magnetic field lines around the magnet. The iron filings are magnetic, which is why they align themselves along the field lines of the magnet.
 b) i) From the North pole of the magnet to the South pole of the magnet, along the magnetic field lines.
   ii) E.g.

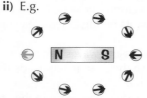

**Q3** a) false
 b) false
 c) true
 d) false
 e) true

**Q4** a) The compass is lined up with the Earth's magnetic field.
 b) His compass is pointing to the Earth's magnetic North pole, which is very close to the Earth's North Pole. So his compass tells him which direction North is. The map also shows which way North is, so he can use the two together to work out where he is.
 c) Lake Barry
 d) Because the compass might point in the wrong direction / point towards the magnet's South pole.

## Pages 69-70 — Electromagnets

**Q1** a) A current flowing through it.
 b) bar magnet
 c) solenoid
 d) i) electromagnet
   ii) Bar magnets always have a magnetic field (you can't turn it off), magnets made from coiled wire can have their magnetic field turned off.

**Q2** a) Steel would stay magnetised when the current was switched off, so you wouldn't be able to turn the electromagnet off.
 b) Soft iron
 c) Increasing the current through the wire, increasing the number of turns in the solenoid/coil.

# Answers

**Q3** Loop of coiled wire — C
Magnet (South pole) — B
Magnet (North pole) — D
Cell — A

**Q4** E.g. normal magnets can't be turned off, so once the metal has been picked up it can't be put down again. Electromagnets can pick the metal up and move it. When they are switched off, the metal is no longer attracted and falls off.

**Q5** E.g. when she closes the switch, the circuit is complete and current flows through the loop of coiled wire. The current causes a magnetic field to form around the wire. Because the wire is already in a magnetic field, there are forces on the loop of wire. These forces act in opposite directions and cause the loop, and the connected propellor, to turn.

## Section 5 — The Earth and Beyond
### Pages 71-72 — Gravity
**Q1** a) newtons (N)
b) gravity
c) These statements should be ticked: The mass of an object never changes, mass is measured in kilograms, mass is the amount of 'stuff' in an object.

**Q2** Everything in the Universe is attracted to everything else by **the force of gravity**.
Gravity keeps the moon **in orbit around the Earth**.
The Earth and the Moon are **attracted to each other**.
The attraction between the Earth and the Sun is bigger than **the attraction between the Earth and the Moon**.

**Q3** a) weaker
b) stronger
c) weaker

**Q4** a)

| Body | Mass of rover (kg) | Gravitational field strength (N/Kg) | Weight of rover (N) |
|------|------|------|------|
| Earth | 1000 | 10 | 10 000 |
| The Moon | 1000 | 1.6 | 1600 |
| Mars | 1000 | 3.7 | 3700 |
| Pluto | 1000 | 0.6 | 600 |

b) Weight = Mass × Gravitational Field Strength
= 1000 kg × 24 N/kg = 24 000 N.
The rover couldn't be used on this planet because the wheels can only support 20 000 N before breaking.

### Pages 73-74 — The Sun and Stars
**Q1** a) A star
b) orbit
c) elliptical / elongated circle
d) Planets don't give out light but stars do.

**Q2** a) A galaxy
b) **Most** of the stars we see at night are in our **galaxy**.
c) billions
d) billions

**Q3** a) by heating, by light
b) E.g. the Sun has strong gravity because it is so massive. The pull of the Sun's gravity keeps all the planets in their orbits.

**Q4** a) Proxima Centauri is the **second closest** star to the Earth.
b) i) E.g. a light year is how far light travels in one year. It is used to measure distance (huge distances between objects in space).
ii) 4 years
c) i) A large collection of stars.
ii) Because it is very far away.

### Pages 75-76 — Day and Night and the Four Seasons
**Q1** a) December 21st
b) September 30th
c) June 21st
d) March 30th / June 21st / September 21st
e) June 21st
f) March 21st and March 30th
g) September 21st and September 30th

**Q2** a) The Earth spins on its **axis** in 24 hours.
b) We call this time one **day**.
c) It takes a **year** for the Earth to complete one revolution of the Sun.
d) We call the track followed by the Earth an **orbit**.
e) The tilt of the Earth's axis causes the **seasons**.
f) In summer, **days** last longer than **nights**.
g) There are **four** seasons every year.

**Q3** a) false
b) false
c) true
d) false
e) false
f) true
g) true

**Q4** a) Scunthorpe and Tehran
b) northern
c) E.g. Johannesburg is in the southern hemisphere and Scunthorpe is in the northern hemisphere. During the summer, the southern hemisphere spends more time in sunlight than it does in darkness. Because the days are longer than nights, there are more hours of sunshine for the land to warm up. The Sun's rays also cover a smaller area of land in Johannesburg than in Scunthorpe in January, so the energy from the Sun is more focused there.

**Answers**

ISBN 978 1 84146 507 4

9 781841 465074

www.cgpbooks.co.uk